'I have inspec
Ramón in a
Aztec workm
of that there is no doubt
has not been licensed by the Society of
Time for importation. We are attempting to establish the mask's provenance,
and once we've identified it we must
then proceed to investigate the effects
of its removal. If we find none, we are
faced with a serious dilemma. We shall
have to determine whether we have a
case of history being changed by interference, and if so whether truth demands
restitution of the former state of
affairs.'

Don Miguel said, 'Father, I'm glad I'm
involved on the practical side of the
Society. My mind boggles at the depth
of these philosophical problems.'

'You may not be so pleased tomorrow,' rumbled the Commander of the
Society of Time. 'We're charging you
with a problem which is deep enough in
its own way. You are to discover the
origin in our time of this mask, and
identify the stranger Higgins bought it
from. And you have two weeks in which
to complete the task.'

TIMES
WITHOUT
NUMBER

JOHN BRUNNER

Hamlyn Paperbacks

TIMES WITHOUT NUMBER
ISBN 0 600 20086 8

This text first published in Great
Britain 1974 by The Elmfield Press
Hamlyn Paperbacks edition 1981

Shorter and substantially different versions of the three
sections of this novel were published separately in *Science
Fiction Adventures* © 1962 by Nova Publications Ltd,
London. The three sections, with numerous minor alterations, were published in book form and copyright ©
1962 by Ace Books Inc., New York.

The present completely revised and considerably ex-
panded text is copyright © 1969 and 1974 by Brunner
Fact and Fiction Ltd.

Hamlyn Paperbacks are published by
The Hamlyn Publishing Group Ltd,
Astronaut House, Feltham,
Middlesex, England

(Paperback Division: Hamlyn Paperbacks
Banda House, Cambridge Grove,
Hammersmith, London W6 0LE)

Printed and bound in Great Britain by
Cox & Wyman Ltd, Reading

This book is sold subject to the condition that it shall not,
by way of trade or otherwise, be lent, re-sold, hired out, or
otherwise circulated without the publisher's prior consent
in any form of binding or cover other than that in which it
is published and without a similar condition including
this condition being imposed on the subsequent
purchaser.

TIMES WITHOUT NUMBER

PART I

SPOIL OF YESTERDAY

ONE

Don Miguel Navarro, Licentiate in Ordinary of the Society of Time and loyal subject of His Most Catholic Majesty Philip IX, *Rey y Imperador*, dodged into a quiet alcove leading off the great hall and breathed a sigh of relief. He had arrived at the party less than an hour before, and already he was wondering how soon he could inconspicuously slip away.

He felt worse than merely disappointed. He felt he'd been cheated.

He had stood in his lodgings a few days ago with an invitation in each hand, wondering which to accept. This whole year of 1988 was one long celebration, of course; since January, balls, parties and festivities galore had been held to mark the four hundredth anniversary of the conquest of England by the mighty Spanish Armada—that key event of history which had saved the Empire from vanishing off the face of the Earth when its homeland was once more overrun by the forces of Islam. Don Miguel was getting rather tired of these affairs, but it was socially wrong to turn down *all* the invitations.

One of the pair he'd had to choose between on this occasion was from the Alcalde of the Municipality of Jorque, who promised clowns, jugglers and a grand pyrotechnical display. Commonplace. He had never been to an official reception in this particular city—in fact, he had only visited Jorque two or three times before—but he doubted whether it would amount to more than a poor copy of what he'd seen in Londres and New Madrid.

The other invitation had a great sprawling signature across the bottom, which could with some difficulty be deciphered as "Catalina di Jorque." And that was what had persuaded him. The Marquesa di Jorque's reputation was not confined to the north of England. She had been a famous beauty in her twenties and thirties; having lost her looks at about the same time as she lost her husband, but having inherited his considerable wealth, she had set up as a successful society hostess and well-known campaigner for female emancipation.

Don Miguel regarded himself as a man of modern and enlightened views. He saw no reason why women should be barred by prejudice from fields traditionally reserved for men, such as philosophy and law. Consequently, feeling rather honoured to have been singled out, he tossed the Alcalde's invitation into the wastebasket and accepted the Marquesa's.

And if things were going to continue as they had up to now, by the end of the evening he'd have turned into a hide-bound reactionary. *Damn* the Marquesa!

It wasn't only the embarrassing experience of being shown off around the hall by her—as it were, a real live time-traveller, exclamation point, in the same tone of voice as one would say,

"A real live tiger!" That happened too often for members of the Society of Time not to have grown used to it; there were, after all, fewer than a thousand of them in the whole of the Empire.

No, his annoyance had a subtler basis. The invitation had referred to "a small gathering of intelligent people," and that was what he had expected. He preferred good conversation to all the clowns and fireworks in the world. But the gathering wasn't small. There were upwards of four hundred people, including clerics, philosophers both pure and natural, musicians, poets, artists and many more.

And they all seemed to be somehow second-rate.

They were a wide enough cross-section, granted. As well as leading lights of Northern English society, he had been presented to visitors from New Castile, on the other side of the Atlantic, all of whom reminded him in silky voices that the Prince of New Castile was the Commander of the Society of Time, except for those who wore the sleek black braids which indicated Indian extraction—they reminded him that the Director of Fieldwork for the Society was a Mohawk. He had also met a couple of fuddled Moors, obviously present as a concrete demonstration of the Marquesa's enlightened tolerance, who had been persuaded to take wine against the injunction of the Prophet and who were becoming very drunk. Don Miguel found that most distasteful.

Second-rate, the lot of them. Clearly the Marquesa's reputation was founded on sand, and if she was the best spokesman—correction: spokeswoman—for sexual equality who could be found in the northern provinces, then it was going to be a long, long time before the movement made any headway!

At least, if Don Miguel Navarro had anything to do with it. He wondered again what chance there was of sneaking out of

the house and finding his way to the venue of the Municipality's reception. Rather their clowns than *these* clowns!

His glass was empty. Looking around for one of the slaves
who were circulating continually among the throng with trays
of full ones, he caught the eye of a slender Guinea-
girl with knowing eyes and active hips, and as he watched her
move away after exchanging his glass he sighed again. There
were so many better ways of wasting time!

The sigh must have been too loud; there came a chuckle
from near where he was standing, and a deep voice with a
humorous edge to it said, "Your honour is perhaps not
accustomed to the Marquesa's entertainments?"

Don Miguel half-turned, and found he was being addressed
by a man of middle height, in a maroon cloak and white velvet
breeches, whose gingery hair was fastidiously dressed high on
his head. There was something rather engaging in his freckled
face.

Giving the semi-bow which etiquette demanded, he said,
"Miguel Navarro. Indeed, it's the first time I've been to one of
these affairs. I'm not a very frequent visitor to Jorque."

"Arcimboldo Ruiz," said the freckled man. "You're the
time-traveller, aren't you?"

Dispiritedly, Don Miguel admitted the charge. Don Arcimboldo gave another chuckle, tinged this time with sympathy.

"I can imagine what Catalina has been putting you through!
It's always the same when she manages to inveigle a celebrity
into attending one of these parties—the poor fellow gets
trundled around from group to group while she basks in her
moment of reflected glory. Right?"

"Only too right," Don Miguel muttered.

"It wouldn't be so bad if she also had the grace to advise
strangers of the best technique for surviving her receptions.

Or maybe she can't. Maybe she doesn't know it herself."

"It would appear that you do," Don Miguel said. "At any rate, you seem to be enjoying yourself."

"Oh, I am! You see, I've known Catalina a long time, and I'm no longer misled by her—what can one term them? —intellectual pretensions, perhaps. As you've probably worked out for yourself by now, with the best will in the world one can't avoid saying that she's over-confident of her own talents. Accordingly one must ignore the wild promises she makes about the fabulous and wonderful guests one's going to encounter here, and concentrate on the genuine advantages— excellent food and occasionally miraculous wine. And if one does run into an interesting stranger, one treats that purely as a bonus."

Don Miguel's face twisted into his crooked smile—always crooked, thanks to a certain Greek hoplite on the plains of Macedonia. "I'd arrived at the same conclusion," he admitted. "Yet it seemed to me improbable. How could all these people be deceived about her for so long?"

Picking a luscious-looking cake off a tray borne by a passing slave, Don Arcimboldo gave a shrug. "How many of them are 'deceived'? Would you be deceived the second time you were sent one of Catalina's invitations? No, I think most of us are here to amuse ourselves rather than our hostess. But it costs little to play up to her in return—a few minutes' flattery will generally suffice, after which one is left to one's own devices."

"That," Don Miguel said from the bottom of his heart, "is a relief."

At that moment, however, another slave—the Marquesa di Jorque was wealthy, and had perhaps a hundred in her household—came searching through the crowd: this time a

tall Guinea-man who towered above the heads of the guests.
Catching sight of Don Miguel, he broke off his hunt and
hurried over.

"Her ladyship requests the pleasure of your honour's
company," he informed Don Miguel with a low bow, then
straightened and stood like an ebony statue awaiting an
answer.

Pulling a wry face at Don Arcimboldo, Don Miguel muttered, "I thought you said one might look forward to being
left to one's own devices?"

Ruefully Don Arcimboldo spread his hands. "It's not quite
the same in your case, is it? After all, there's something very
special about a man who has travelled in time."

"I—ah—I don't suppose I could tell him to go back and say
he can't find me?" Don Miguel suggested hopefully.

"It wouldn't be fair. He'd incur a bout of Catalina's wrath,
which can be both spectacular and public. The poor fellow
would probably spend the night in chains."

"You mean her egalitarian views don't extend beyond
women and Moors?"

"No. Not by a very long way."

"That's what I was afraid of," Don Miguel grunted. "Oh
well, I suppose I'd better comply." He tossed back the last of
his drink, and as he turned to follow the slave added formally
to Don Arcimboldo, "This meeting has much honoured me.
May we meet again."

"The honour is mine. May we meet again."

TWO

The Marquesa was standing under a bower of hot-house creepers trained on silver branches, deep in conversation with two men. One of them Don Miguel recognised: Father Peabody, whose official post was that of a clerk to the Archbishop of Jorque but who was commonly known as "her ladyship's chaplain". People whispered unkind speculations about his function in her household. The other was a stranger to him.

"Ah, Don Miguel!" exclaimed the Marquesa when he halted before her, and flashed a look that had probably laid her suitors low in swathes when she was twenty years younger. "I trust that I have not dragged you away at an untimely juncture! But we are speaking of a difficult problem, and would welcome your expert opinion. Let Don Marco propose the matter to you."

She gestured at the man Don Miguel did not know, a

foppish person in a moss-green cloak and yellow breeches, whose sword-hilt was so heavily encrusted with jewels it was obvious the weapon was not intended for use but only show. He uttered his name in a high goat-like bleat.

"Marco Villanova, your honour!"

"Miguel Navarro," said Don Miguel briefly. "What is this problem of yours?"

"We were disputing regarding the private lives of the great, Don Miguel. It is my contention—indeed, reason demands it!—that the greatness of individuals must be manifest as much in their private as in their public lives."

"We spoke, in particular, of Julius Caesar," said Father Peabody, rubbing his hands on the front of his long black cassock. "There is a man whose greatness is not in dispute, I venture to claim."

He spoke with a broad flat local accent, and bobbed his head humbly after every other word as though over-conscious of his inferior social status.

"Well, as to Caesar," said Don Miguel, a little more snappishly than he had intended because he was so irritated at being sent for on such a petty excuse, "I can give you accurate information. As it happens, I've spoken to him. I found him to be a perfumed fop. In his youth, he was guilty of abominations with men, and in his maturity his promiscuous behaviour was such that the gossip of all Rome centred on it. If this was greatness in his private life, you may maintain so; I would not."

Don Marco flushed and drew back half a pace, with a sidelong glance at the Marquesa. "It does not seem fitting to speak of such matters in the hearing of a lady!" he exclaimed.

"Kindly refrain from blaming me—blame rather Caesar himself," Don Miguel answered frigidly. "Her ladyship asked my expert opinion, and I've given it. History is an impartial force, Don Marco; it has no patience with those dabblers who prefer to turn aside from what displeases them, and it's full of unpleasant but inescapable facts."

Don Marco's flush deepened still further, and—after a moment's debate with herself—the Marquesa gave an emphatic nod.

"Indeed, Don Marco, Don Miguel is perfectly correct to say this. It is the fruit of a false prejudice which has led to us women being sheltered and pampered and, not to mince words, *lied to* about the nature of the world! It suits the interests of overweening men to invest us with a weakness we don't possess!"

She raised her sharp eyes to Don Miguel's face, and heaved a sigh. "But that we have in our midst a man who has spoken with Caesar! Is it not miraculous?"

"We of the Society of Time do not regard it as such," Don Miguel answered, already regretting that he had made his little boast. "It's an application of natural laws, nothing more. A miracle, perhaps, would be to discover a means of flying to the moon. No one has yet suggested how that might be accomplished."

"With—with respect, Don Miguel!" said Father Peabody, bobbing his round head in which his eyes were even rounder. "How was it possible for you to *talk* with Caesar? I understood, if you will pardon me, that the rules of your Society forbid interference, and limit the activity of time-travellers to simple observation!"

I knew I shouldn't have opened my mouth in this kind of company...

The thought flickered across Don Miguel's mind and left a trail of self-directed irritation. But it was too late now to do

other than answer the cleric's sharp question. Anyway, the
published data on the Society's investigation of Rome themselves implied how the trick was worked, and a truly astute
man would not have needed to inquire.

He said wearily, "I assure you, Father, the rules are most
strictly adhered to. It does not, however, constitute interference if a notable historical personage utters words he
would have uttered anyway in the hearing of a person he does
not know and will naturally never meet again. Does that make
the method clear?"

Father Peabody gave a succession of vigorous nods, and
there was a short silence. The Marquesa broke it at last.

"I may be only a poor stupid woman," she said, and
paused, as though waiting for automatic contradiction. Not
getting it, she shot a venomous glare at Father Peabody but
was forced to continue.

"To me," she resumed, "it seems that interference with the
past is out of the question. What was, was! How can it be
changed by our intervention?"

Don Miguel repressed a desire to scowl even more fiercely
than she had just done. For all her vaunted intellectual
accomplishments, the Marquesa had framed a question which
no fifteen-year-old schoolboy of average intelligence would
have wasted breath on. He would have been taught the answer
in class, or pieced it together himself from items in the news.
Indeed, even Don Marco—who did not strike Don Miguel as
exceptionally bright—showed visible surprise at hearing it.

"The basic arguments, my lady," Don Miguel said reluc-
tantly, "are rather a matter for speculative philosophers than
for a pragmatic person like myself. But I have some conception of them, and if you wish I'll try and elucidate."

A shadow of discomfort, as though caused by the realisation that she had let herself in for some heavy brainwork, crossed the Marquesa's face. But she composed herself and adopted an expression of polite interest.

"Do so, if you will," she murmured.

"Very well." Don Miguel hesitated, trying to cast his thoughts into words suitable for her. "To begin with, there are, are there not, in history certain crucial turning-points? Yet each of these in turn was composed of the sum of vast numbers of individual acts and attitudes, and it's rare that we can fine down any event in history to the point of being able to attribute it to one unique causative factor. The majority stem from such a wide spectrum of influences that we cannot grasp the entire range—effectively, therefore, we must regard them as random. The fall of Rome, for instance, was not only due to the invasion of a barbarian horde; it was also due to decadence among the Romans which prevented them from offering much resistance."

The Marquesa nodded. She was beginning to frown, but Don Miguel continued on the assumption that she was not yet out of her depth.

"This vast flow, or stream, of events tending towards a crisis might be compared, in one sense, to a river. The presence or absence of a single pebble on the river's bed will make no significant difference to the course of the waters, and no detectable difference to the level along the bank. Detectable or not, however, it is a difference—*a priori!* Therefore one may also compare the time-flow to an avalanche. It is not beyond the bounds of possibility that something done by a visitor from the future might serve to stay the first stone that triggered the landslide, and thus turn history into another course. If that happened, we might rule ourselves out of existence! One key idea planted in the mind of a

Roman of the year 300 might, for all we are able to predict, result in the defeat of Alaric and the survival of the Roman Empire!"

"I'm *fascinated* by the great empires of the past!" said the Marquesa with enthusiasm. "Especially by—"

She noted the look of annoyance on Don Miguel's face, and broke off. "I was carried away," she concluded apologetically. "Do go on!"

"You've followed me so far?" Don Miguel countered.

"Ye-es . . . Except that if something we did were to change history, how would history have been changed? I mean, without us having gone back to change it?"

With great effort, Don Miguel said patiently, "The question simply wouldn't arise! This would *be* history. It would be all the history there was."

Father Peabody shook his head, a look of resigned wonder on his face. "Truly the ways of the Lord are inscrutable!" he said.

The Marquesa gave a sudden nod and smile. "I see!" she said, and then added doubtfully, "I think . . ."

Don Marco spoke up. "Are there not, though, crisis points in history where regardless of what we were or were not to do the outcome would be little affected?"

"Oh, certainly," agreed Don Miguel. "The classic example, of course, is one which we all know—the storm which broke the English defences four hundred years ago, doused their fireships, and in effect made certain the conquest of Britain. Men could hardly interfere with the brewing of a storm! Even in cases such as that, however, it's imperative to be very, very discreet."

"Oh, surely the result was a foregone conclusion in any case!" objected the Marquesa. "I mean, the Armada was so huge and so well-armed . . ."

"I can assure you, my lady, we have studied the matter exhaustively. The most eminent strategists and naval authorities agree that encumbered as they were with occupation troops and supplies the galleons might well have been worsted—especially if the English fireships had got among them with a steady following wind. No, it's well established that it was the fortunate coincidence of the storm breaking which tipped the scales of battle to our side."

"I think I follow," said Don Marco, frowning. "What must not under any circumstances be done in such an instance, therefore, is to—well, to cause a delay in the arrival of the fleet, so that the storm has already blown over. Am I right?"

"Yes, precisely so."

"To think that we hang by such a thread!" marvelled Father Peabody aloud.

It would have suited Don Miguel to perfection if at this point he had been able to snap the thread tying him to the Marquesa; however, she was determined not to let that happen yet. Stretching out one heavily beringed hand to touch his arm, she said, "Now there's something else, Don Miguel, which I must take this opportunity of asking you. I've heard that in this quatrocentennial year your Society has permitted certain especially favoured outsiders to witness the actual victory—is this so?"

"No, of course it's not!" Don Miguel was genuinely shocked. "From whom did you hear such nonsense? The rules of the Society are absolutely inflexible: only Licentiates are permitted to travel back in time. The purpose of time-travel is serious historical research; it's not a—a carnival, a spectacle for sensation-seekers!"

"Curious," mused the Marquesa. "I had been assured . . .

But no matter! Yet I find it in my heart to wish the rule was not so rigid. I have such a burning desire to assist at some great happening of the past."

"We have brought back pictures—" began Don Miguel.

"Ah, pictures! Pictures are flat and lifeless! What are pictures beside a view of reality? But your heart is hard, Don Miguel. I see that."

"My lady, time-travel is far from a pleasure trip. The dirt, the squalor, the cruelty, the—the disgusting facts of life in earlier ages, in short, account for that."

"Ah, but dirt and squalor are still with us. Why, yonder in the market outside the city wall of Jorque itself, there are people infested with lice, who probably don't know the meaning of the word soap! I have no desire to view *their* ancestors—they were doubtless the same fifty generations ago. But I would greatly love to see the splendours of the past. As I began to say earlier"—she punctuated the sentence with an arch look of reproach that belonged in the armoury of a far younger woman—"I am most fascinated by the empires of bygone days. The empire of Mexico, for instance, with its wonderful goldwork and featherwork!"

"And its pleasant custom of sacrificing human beings by tearing out the living heart and displaying it to the victim," sourly responded Don Miguel.

"Have you no romance in you?" cried the Marquesa.

"It is not I that lack romance; it is the empires of the past you so admire."

"And yet . . ." She let the words trail away and gave a delicate, lady-like shrug. "Well, I confess I called for your expert opinion, and since you've given it I cannot do otherwise than accept what you tell me. Nonetheless, let me at least show you on what grounds I base my admiration. I have a new treasure, a golden mask of Aztec manufacture—I'd like to show it off to you and see if I cannot persuade you that there were *some* fine things in the olden days."

"If you're seeking my expert opinion on that also, I'm afraid I can't oblige you," Don Miguel countered. "I know little of goldwork or jewellery."

"Ah, but no one could fail to be impressed by my great mask! Come!"

She clapped her hands, and the tall Guinea-man who attended on her hurried to clear them a way through the throng.

THREE

"I trust you will not think it brazen of me," said the Marquesa, "when I tell you it's in my bedchamber that I've hung the mask. I feel it's an insult to the dignity of women to assume they cannot protect their own virtue if they happen to be in the same room as both a man and a bed."

By this time she had practically succeeded in making the enlightened and progressive Don Miguel into a conservative bigot; accordingly he retorted, "You must admit it's equally an insult to us men, my lady, if you assume we are inevitably inclined to make improper advances."

The Marquesa's lips tightened to a thin white line; then she forced herself to relax.

"True, true! One who pleads for equality between the sexes cannot do other than agree."

But she looked extremely unhappy at having to do so.

In the wake of the Guinea-man they left the crowded

reception hall and passed along a corridor where their footsteps echoed on magnificent Moorish tiling, until they came to a room whose door their accompanying slave opened with a key from a chain at his waist. The interior was large and luxurious, dominated by a great bed disguised as a bank of green moss. The walls and ceilings were festooned with the Marquesa's beloved creepers, and an adjacent bathroom was revealed through a half-curtained gap on the far side.

But after the first glance Don Miguel saw nothing more of the room. His whole attention was riveted by the gleaming mask mounted on the wall facing the foot of the bed. Hardly daring to breathe, he walked over and stood gazing at it.

It was indeed, as the Marquesa claimed, magnificent. And it was more than merely a mask. It was a representation in beaten gold of the head-dress, face and shoulder-plates of an Aztec warrior. The square, snarling face was nine inches deep, the head-dress was twice as high, and the shoulder-plates were a good fifteen inches on each side. It nearly dizzied him with its rich yellow lustre.

"Ah, you're capable of being impressed after all!" exclaimed the Marquesa. "I'd begun to imagine you lacked all traces of emotion! Am I not justified in feeling proud of it?"

Don Miguel put out his hand to touch the thing, half hoping it would prove to be a mere illusion. But the heavy metal was solid and cool to his fingers. He stepped back, his mind in a whirl as he noted the signs of genuine Aztec workmanship the mask bore.

"Why do you not say anything?" the Marquesa cried.

Don Miguel found his voice and heard it creak like the rusty hinges of a cellar-door.

"All I can say, my lady, is this. I hope to high heaven that it's forged."

"What?" She took an astonished pace towards him. "No, of course it's not a forgery!"

"I tell you it had better be. For if it is not . . ." He could not complete the utterance; his mind quailed before the implications.

"But why do you say such a thing?"

"Because this is perfect, my lady. As perfect as though the goldsmith finished work today. Therefore it is not a buried relic dug up from the ground and restored. No restorer of the present time could so precisely adopt the Aztec style. A forger might—just—achieve a uniform pseudo-Aztec style over the whole of a work like this, if he had long steeped himself in the period."

"But I don't want it to be a forgery!" The Marquesa was almost in tears all of a sudden. "No, I'm certain that it's genuine!"

"In that case," Don Miguel said ruthlessly, "I must take possession of it in the name of the Society of Time, as contraband mass illegally imported to the present!"

How much does that thing weigh? Twelve pounds? Fifteen?

When every single grain of dust gathered by a time-traveller had to be beaten and shaken from his clothing before he made his return, what might not a theft of that size from the past mean in terms of changes in history?

"Where did you get it?" he pressed. The Marquesa, stunned, glared at him and ignored his question.

"You're joking!" she accused. "It's a cruel joke!"

"No, my lady, it's a long way from joking, I'm afraid. It's as well for you that the first Licentiate of the Society to hear about this thing is under your roof as a guest and obligated by your hospitality. Otherwise I can't guess the consequences. Don't you realise that offences concerning temporal contraband come directly under the jurisdiction of the Holy Office?"

All the colour drained out of the Marquesa's face bar the artificial smears of rouge on lips and cheeks. She said faintly, "But how can one be—be punished for accepting a gift?"

Ah. The words made it clear to Don Miguel that she had in fact suspected the mask might be contraband; it would have been surprising if she had not, since anyone with the intelligence of an average two-year-old would have jumped to that conclusion. It could only have been a combination of vanity and alcohol which led her to show the thing off to him. Now she was deeply regretting the impulse.

"A gift!" he repeated. "Did you inquire about this *gift* at the Society's office here in Jorque? Did you check whether it had been licensed for importation?"

"No, of course not! Why should I?"

Don Miguel bit back the answer which rose to his lips; there was no point in angering her further. Adopting a more conciliatory tone, he said, "I see. You realised it was an import, but you took the existence of the license for granted?"

"Why—why, yes!" She put her hands to her temples and swayed.

"Who gave it to you, then?"

"A—a friend!"

"My lady, it would be better to tell me than an Inquisitor . . wouldn't it?"

"Are you threatening me?"

"No, you are threatening me, and the existence of our entire world! Get that fact into your head, my lady—there's plenty of room for it, since your skull's so empty!" Don Miguel didn't enjoy this descent to crude insult, but there seemed to be no alternative.

"Don—Don Arcimboldo Ruiz!" She choked over the name. Don Miguel whirled, his cloak flying, and snapped at the tall slave waiting by the door.

"Find him! Bring him here—and quickly!"

Upon the slave's departure, the Marquesa threw herself across the bed and dissolved into ostentatious weeping. Don Miguel ignored her, and passed the time until Don Arcimboldo's arrival in inspecting the mask more closely. Everything pointed to the conclusion he had already reached, particularly the freshness of the marks left by the goldsmith's hammer. Nothing buried in the earth and recovered—not even incorruptible gold—could have retained this condition throughout the centuries.

"Heaven preserve us," Don Miguel whispered under his breath.

Abruptly the door was flung back again, and the freckled man whom he'd encountered earlier came hurrying into the room, wearing a puzzled expression.

"Don Miguel!" he exclaimed. "You desired my presence?" And appended a bow to the Marquesa, who had sat up again at the intrusion and was desperately wiping away the trace of tears.

Don Miguel wasted no time on formality. "She says you gave her this mask—is that true?"

"Why . . . Yes, certainly I did. Is something wrong?"

"Where did you get it?"

"I bought it openly enough, from a merchant in the market beyond the city wall. From a man named Higgins, to be precise, with whom I've done much business in the past."

"Did you check that it was licensed for importation?"

"No, what reason would I have to do such a thing?" A look

of awe spread across Don Arcimboldo's face. "Oh no! You're not implying that it's . . .?"

"Contraband? It certainly seems to be." Don Miguel passed a worried hand through his hair, ruining the careful pre-party endeavours of his barber. "I don't doubt you acted in good faith, but . . . Oh, honestly, Don Arcimboldo! Look at that thing, will you? It must weigh more than twelve pounds; it's so finely wrought it *must* have been famous in its own period, and it would certainly have come to my notice if the Society had licensed it for importation. Anyway, we wouldn't *dispose* of something like that—we'd donate it to the Imperial Museum, or the Mexicological Institute in New Madrid. Didn't its mere condition make you suspect something might be wrong?"

"Ah . . . Well, frankly, no." Don Arcimboldo shifted from foot to foot, but in his position, Don Miguel told himself, he too would have been embarrassed. "I'm afraid I'm not much of an expert on New World artefacts; I collect Saxon, Irish and Norse work. Which is why I didn't hang on to the mask, of course."

"But surely anyone with an interest in any kind of . . ."

Don Miguel let the words trail away. There was no point in arguing. Far more important was to put right the consequences of this disaster, if—and he shivered a little at the implications of the proviso—it were still possible to detect them.

"Is there anything I can do?" Don Arcimboldo inquired anxiously.

"Yes. Yes, there is. Find a couple of slaves and send them to the local branches of the Holy Office and the Society of Time, and get someone discreet and capable here as fast as possible. It's going to spoil the party somewhat, I'm afraid, but better a party than the world!"

Even as he spoke he was aware that from his own point of view it would be as bad to be shown wrong as to be shown right—the Society did not take kindly to people who cried wolf in public about its private affairs. But there was no help for that now; to employ the image he'd used earlier in explaining temporal paradox to the Marquesa, there was a key stone for every avalanche, and in this particular case he'd just knocked it loose and it was rolling.

Imaginary thunder grumbled in his ears.

FOUR

When, a week later, he was bidden to attend at a meeting in the Chamber of Full Council of the Society of Time—the first occasion he had set foot within it—Don Miguel had still not been informed whether his inspired deductions had been correct. It was therefore with considerable apprehension that he took his place and looked around.

The atmosphere of the Chamber was rich with a sense of authority and ritual, like the interior of a great cathedral—which in many ways it resembled. It was panelled with fine dark woods inlaid with gold; most of its floor-space was occupied by four tables arranged in the shape of two capital L's, with gaps at diagonally opposite corners. These tables were draped with dark red velvet; chairs ranged along them were upholstered in the same material, except for one which was still vacant. That was purple, the prince's colour, and it stood at the eastern end of the room, transfixed like a butterfly on a pin by a shaft of pure white light stabbing down from the ceiling. Another shaft of light, focused horizontally, completed a cross at twice a man's height from the floor.

Along the northern table, robed, cowled, and in shadow, were ranged five persons whom Don Miguel knew to be the General Officers of the Society. But at present he was unable to tell which of them was which. Behind them, immobile, their private secretaries stood dutifully awaiting their masters' orders.

He himself was seated in the middle of the western side of the oblong formed by the tables, while on the southern side, opposite the General Officers, were . . . What to call them? One could hardly say they were prisoners, even if they had been brought here under guard, for as yet there had been no trial nor even any official charges. Perhaps one could call them "the witnesses"—but then he too was a witness.

At all events, they comprised the Marquesa, attended by two of her personal maids, Don Arcimboldo, who was alone, and the merchant Higgins from whom the Aztec mask had been purchased. The Marquesa had been weeping, Higgins was plainly terrified to the point of petrifaction, but Don Arcimboldo had an air of puzzled boredom, as though he was certain that this stupid misunderstanding would shortly be regulated.

And, on the velvet-covered table in front of the vacant purple chair, the mask itself rested like a great golden toad.

Suddenly there was a ring of trumpets, and the air seemed to grow tense. There was movement behind the empty chair, at the eastern doorway of the Chamber. A herald garbed in cloth-of-gold strode forward and spoke in a voice much resembling the tone of the trumpets which had just sounded.

"Be upstanding for His Highness the Prince of New Castile, by His Majesty's direction Commander of the Society of Time!"

All those present in the room rose to their feet and bowed.

When they were told in a grunting voice to sit down again, the Prince had already taken his place. Previously Don Miguel had only seen the Commander of the Society from a distance, at official functions in public where he was surrounded by his enormous retinue and there was small chance of a mere Licentiate getting to close quarters with him. Accordingly he studied him with interest, seeing a round man with stubby limbs and a short black beard; a ring of baldness was spreading on his scalp. He wore the full-dress uniform of a Knight of the Holy Roman Empire, and his chest glittered with the stars of all the orders which he as a Prince of the Blood had accumulated. The total effect was impressive; it was meant to be.

His face was partly in shadow because the light was above him, but it was possible to discern that his eyes had turned at once in Don Miguel's direction, and after a few seconds the latter began to feel uncomfortable, as though he were under the scrutiny of an inquisitor. He resisted the temptation to fidget in his chair.

At last the grunting voice came again, like a saw rasping into fresh oak-planks.

"You're Navarro, are you?"

"I am, sir," said Don Miguel, finding that his mouth was dry. Having reviewed his actions many times during the past few days, he was convinced he had acted correctly according to the strict rules of the Society. Yet there still remained the nagging possibility that the General Officers might put a different interpretation on the facts . . .

"And this bauble in front of me is the thing that all the fuss is about, I suppose? Hah!" The Prince leaned forward and stretched out his thick fingers, that sprouted coarse black hair along their backs. His touch on the mask was almost a caress. Plainly, he liked it—or he liked the fine gold of which it was made.

At last he sat back and shot a keen glance in the direction of the prisoners before turning to the cowled and shadowed line of General Officers.

"This is for you, I think, Father Ramón," he said.

Don Miguel watched to see which of the hitherto anonymous officers would reply. He had never met, but he had heard over and over since childhood about Father Ramón, the Jesuit, the master-theoretician of the Society and the greatest living expert on the nature of time and the philosophical implications of travelling through it.

"I have inspected the object," said the figure on the Prince's immediate right in a dry, precise voice. "It is of Aztec workmanship and Mexican gold—of that there is no doubt at all. And it has not been licensed by the Society for importation."

Don Miguel felt a surge of relief. At least he had been correct on that score, then.

"The consequences of this temporal contraband cannot as yet be fully assessed," the Jesuit continued. "We are attempting to establish the mask's provenance to within a few years—its condition is so good, we should have little difficulty in assigning it to at least its city of origin and perhaps even to one particular workshop in that city. Once we've identified it we must then proceed to investigate the effects of its removal. If we find none, we are faced with a serious dilemma."

"How so?" demanded the Prince, leaning back and twisting a little sideways in his chair.

"*Imprimis*," said Father Ramón, and thrust forward a thin finger from out of darkness to lay it on the table, "we shall have to determine whether we have in fact replaced it where it came from. And if we have replaced it, then we shall have to establish the time at which it was replaced, and the circumstances. And *secundo*, we shall have to determine—if it has not been replaced—whether we have in fact a case of history being changed."

Shorn of much of its complexity by this cleanly logic, the problem nonetheless struck Don Miguel as terrifying.

"You mean"—it startled him to find that he was speaking, but since all present were turning towards him, he ploughed on—"you mean, Father, that we may find its disappearance incorporated in our *new* history as an accomplished fact, with no record of the history which the theft has altered?"

The faceless head gazed at him. "Your presumption," said the Jesuit coldly, and hesitated, so that Don Miguel had a little while in which to wonder in what sense he was using the word presumption, "is—correct."

Don Miguel murmured a barely audible word of thanks and resolved to hold his tongue until next spoken to.

"May we leave the technical aspects of this in the hands of your staff, then, Father?" the Prince inquired.

"I think for the moment that will be the wisest course. Immediately I have further information, I will relay it to the Council for a decision."

"Good!" The Prince seemed very pleased at abandoning that portion of the discussion, and turned at once to another which appeared to interest him more. "We come now to the associated problems which have been entailed by this affair. To begin with—Navarro!"

The last word was uttered in so sharp a bark that Don Miguel jumped.

"Navarro, what possessed you to arrest the Marquesa di Jorque when she was so plainly an innocent party in this case?"

Don Miguel's heart sank so rapidly he could almost feel it arriving in his boots. He said stiffly, "I acted, sir, in strict accordance with the law and the rules of the Society."

"Heaven's name, man! Didn't anyone ever tell you that to stick rigidly to the letter of the law is the mark of a man without imagination? I've studied the information laid before me, and it's perfectly clear that her ladyship acted throughout in unquestionable good faith. I'm discharging her from custody here and now, and I require you to apologise to her before she returns to her domains at Jorque."

What?

There was no hope of arguing with the Commander of the Society, especially not in the presence of outsiders, but Don Miguel was horrified. Was not the law, in both letter and spirit, mankind's chief bulwark against the forces of chaos? Even from a Prince of the Blood he could not accept an order to apologise for acting in accordance with the law!

He grew aware that everyone was waiting for him to comply. The invisible faces of the General Officers were turned to stare at him, and the Marquesa, suddenly repossessed of her usual poise, was glaring at him triumphantly, tapping her manicured fingers on the arm of her chair.

To cover his uncertainty, he rose slowly to his feet. By the time he was erect he had decided what to say.

"Sir, with all respect to you as a Prince and my Commander, I will not apologise to the Marquesa for doing as the law lays down. I *will* apologise for not realising that she is an innocent."

An innocent. A simpleton, in other words. He hoped the distinction would penetrate.

It did. The Marquesa stiffened with fury and the countenance of the Prince began to purple; Don Miguel braced himself for the impact of his royal wrath. But the tension broke suddenly—broke against a thin, rather high-pitched laugh. With amazement Don Miguel realised it came from Father Ramón.

"Commander, that is an apology exactly meet for the case," the Jesuit exclaimed. "Surely anyone but an innocent would have wondered how so magnificent an artefact came to be on sale instead of in a museum?"

The Prince thought that over for a moment. Eventually he gave a tentative chuckle, and the chuckle developed into an outright laugh in which the other General Officers joined. To the accompaniment of their mirth the Marquesa hastened from the hall, her shoulders bowed with humiliation.

Don Miguel, surprised by so easy a victory, slowly resumed his chair.

"Well!" the Prince said at length. "I suppose I can look forward now to an almighty row with my cousin the Duchess of Jorque—but never mind, Father, you were perfectly correct about Navarro's apology, as I realise now I think it over. It would be a good thing, though, if we sorted the rest of the matter out before the storm breaks; at least I'd have a chance to argue back!" He raised a stern finger to point to Don Miguel. "Since you triggered the crisis, I trust you've taken steps of your own to sort it out? For instance, have you discovered where the mask came from in our own time?"

More than ever uncertain of himself, because it struck him as somehow unfitting for a Prince of the Blood to refer so casually to the likelihood of a family quarrel, Don Miguel said, "Ah—well, sir, as you know, Don Arcimboldo Ruiz bought the mask from the merchant Higgins, who is present. And the latter maintains that he in his turn acquired it from a stranger who called at his shop in the market outside Jorque."

"Yes, I've already been told about this." The Prince turned thoughtful eyes on Higgins, who tried to sink through the seat of his chair; he was a middle-aged man without great personality. "Concerning this stranger, then! What proof did he offer that he was legally in possession of the mask?"

The merchant glanced from side to side as though seeking a way of escape. Finding none, he babbled in the flat broad accent that Peabody exhibited also, and most of the people in the north of England, "Your highness, I swear! I swear what I said is true! I bought it from a stranger, on the first day of April as I recall."

"Are you always so ready to do business with strangers?"

"Sir, never! Never in my life before!" Higgins's voice dropped to a bare whisper. "I can only say I must have been mad—must have had a brainstorm, your highness! For I cannot recall the man's face, and I failed to enter his name in my account-book! Never in my life have I done any such thing before—ask anyone who knows me in Jorque, they'll say I'm a respectable merchant and—"

"Enough!" Curtly the Prince cut short the stammered flow of words. "Navarro, have you investigated the fellow's story?"

"I have, sir. And it does seem to be true that up till now Higgins has been a man of excellent reputation. I've spoken to several people who have sold or pawned him goods, and they say he has always been careful to ascertain they had proper title to what they were offering. He has had a number of extratemporal objects through his hands—small curios not worth space in a museum—and the office of the Society in Jorque has always found him scrupulously careful about checking the importation licence."

"Yet this time he buys contraband from a total stranger! He must indeed have had a brainstorm!"

"And sold it to me, your highness!" Don Arcimboldo spoke up diffidently. "To me who had no reason for questioning his right to its possession."

The Prince shrugged. "That's as may be, Don Arcimboldo —one still wonders why you didn't suspect it of being imported illegally. Still, I grant that Higgins's alleged respectability would have disinclined you to investigate."

"Sir." A single flat word from one of the hitherto silent General Officers. Don Miguel tensed, for even that one word betrayed the unmistakable accent of a Mohawk. His guess at the speaker's identity was confirmed in the next second by the Prince.

"Yes, Red Bear?"

The Director of Fieldwork for the Society! They'd really brought the big guns to bear on this case!

"A motion, sir," Red Bear grunted. "That the merchant be further interrogated. That Don Arcimboldo be discharged as an innocent party. That we continue in private session to discuss what has passed."

There was a murmur of agreement from his colleagues. The Prince slapped his palm on the table with a sound like a pistol-shot.

"So resolved! Clear the room," he added in a lower tone to his personal aide.

Don Miguel made to rise, but the Prince motioned him back to his seat with a frown, and he complied with a sense of apprehension. It was not exactly normal practice for a lowly

Licentiate of the Society with a mere four years of service and five field trips to his credit to be invited to sit in during a confidential meeting of the General Officers.

Someone—and from his just-uttered remarks it might well be Red Bear—was obviously taking this matter very seriously indeed.

FIVE

As soon as all non-members of the Society had left the Chamber and the doors had been locked with a great slamming of heavy bolts, the lights went up and the officers relaxed in their chairs, shaking back the cowls from their heads. Don Miguel was almost surprised to discover that in full illumination the Chamber was just a room—large, palatial, but simply a room. And, equally, the General Officers were ordinary men. There was exceptional character and experience stamped on their faces; nonetheless, they were men.

He found himself able to relax a little also.

The Prince fumbled a large pipe from a pouch at his belt and stuffed it with tobacco in coarse-cut hunks. Lighting it, he mumbled around the stem.

"Well, young Navarro, I don't mind telling you that you put the cat in the pigeoncote with this rash act of yours!"

A harsh grunt, as though to say "understatement!", came from Red Bear, whose long Indian face was framed in elegantly dressed black braids as slick as oil.

Father Ramón, seated between Red Bear and the Prince, passed a thin hand over his bald cranium in a way that suggested he had acquired in youth the habit of running his fingers through his hair and still expected subconsciously to find some on his scalp. His face reminded Don Miguel of a bird, with the skin stretched tight around a beaky nose and little, very bright eyes.

He said quietly, "Sir, it may have been an unavoidable cat."

The Prince shrugged, his pipe pouring out smoke like a bonfire. "I'd be inclined to dispute that . . . if I didn't know better than to dispute with one of your Order, Father! What I mean, though, is what I say: I hold that Navarro has caused us a deal of unnecessary botheration."

The Jesuit looked worried. "Again, I can't agree. In my view he has so far acted sensibly, apart from taking the Marquesa di Jorque into custody." He turned to face Don Miguel directly.

"How old are you, my son?"

"Ah . . . I'm nearly thirty, Father."

"In that case you should by now be better able to judge people. I think five minutes' conversation with the Marquesa should have sufficed to inform you that she would never in a million years have thought to inquire of the Society's office about the mask she'd been given. Like a child with a new toy, she'd have been too afraid of losing it."

It hardly seemed to Don Miguel that the greed of a fading beauty should be allowed to excuse an infringement of the Society's rules; however, he was glad that the Jesuit's reproof had been so mild, and held his peace.

"On the other hand," Father Ramón continued, "I confess I'm greatly puzzled by the story which the merchant tells. I seem to recall seeing in his deposition that our brother Navarro admitted feeling annoyed with the Marquesa because she was showing him off like a performing animal to her other guests. That remark struck home, because—as I hardly need to remind you—the work of the Society itself runs the risk of being turned into a mere spectacle for sensation-seekers."

Like a spark and gunpowder, two facts came together in Don Miguel's mind and shot him forward on his chair. He said explosively, "Then it's true!"

The curious gaze of the General Officers fixed on him again, but only Father Ramón seemed to understand the comment without explanation. He said, "You have heard about this disgrace to the Society?"

"Hah!" said Red Bear. "If it stopped there! If that were all!"

"Then it *is* true?" pressed Don Miguel. "But how could such a thing be allowed to happen?"

The Prince coughed. "Father, as usual I'll defer to your judgement—but is this wholly wise?"

"To give our brother the facts? I think so. In the matter currently before us he's displayed considerable moral courage—it's not every Licentiate who would have defied a powerful noblewoman, alas!" Having delivered himself of this verdict, the Jesuit turned back to Don Miguel and resumed.

"You asked how such a thing could be *allowed* to happen! Well, it is of course not allowed; on the contrary it's completely forbidden. However, certain Licentiates have stumbled on a trick which has thus far enabled them to escape retribution—though I promise you when they're discovered their licences will last an even shorter time than their freedom! You must be acquainted with the normal operation of time apparatus, but are you familiar with the effect of increasing the spatial components of the drive-field?"

Don Miguel frowned. He said, "Superficially, Father; I mean, I know that proper choice of factors permits objects to be drawn into a time-field from a distance or set down at a distance from the apparatus's location . . . Oh!"

"I think you understand what I'm referring to," Father Ramón said, pleased. "The trick I mentioned works after this fashion, then. The corruptible Licentiates accept payment secretly from clients who wish to witness the victory of the Armada, or the Coliseum games, or the Battle of the Guinea Coast, or the disgusting acts in the temples of Egypt—or whatever—and then plan an innocent field-trip, which is approved as routine by our brother Red Bear. This trip is always to a more distant time than their real destination. They then collect their clients from a time and place when the latter are unobserved, deliver them where they want to be, continue to conduct their fieldwork further back, and rejoin their clients on the way back to the present—where, naturally, they replace them at the very second of their departure. Put so elaborately, it seems complicated; in effect, it can be devilishly simple. Who can tell, for instance, from which direction a traveller through time is arriving?"

"And people are using the Society's own time apparatus for this—this *knavery*?" Don Miguel's mind was reeling with the impact of the Jesuit's revelation.

"They would hardly dare to construct illicit apparatus of their own, easy though that might be. And why should they, anyhow? This had been going on for well over a year before we realised."

"Had—had many of us been tempted to take bribes?"

The Jesuit hesitated. Finally he said in a gruff tone, "More than thirty Licentiates are under investigation because their incomes are disproportionately high."

"Thirty!" Don Miguel's dismay registered in his voice. The Prince, finding that his pipe had gone out, felt for means to relight it and spoke up gloomily.

"It wouldn't be so bad if all that was involved were—uh —*unofficial observation.* I mean, I've taken my father on the odd trip myself, without any harm being done."

"But that's not quite the same thing," Don Miguel said slowly. The Prince chuckled.

"Yes, kings get away with a good deal! But as I've often been told by Father Ramón—very rightly—divine law doesn't recognise royalty as something special. *I* know that. The people we're talking about, unfortunately, seem not to. It seems that they've allowed some of these illegal travellers to bring back souvenirs of their trip."

Father Ramón nodded. "Of which this great golden mask is presumably one."

A chill passed down Don Miguel's spine. He said, "Is there then a—a regular trade in such contraband? Why, the implications are incalculable!"

"True," confirmed Father Ramón. "Luckily, however, this is as yet the largest single item we've run across; the remainder have been intrinsically valueless, mere curios." He leaned back and set his fingertips together, elbows on the arms of his chair.

"Were it nothing more than household garbage, though, we would still need to be worried about the importation of anything we hadn't licensed. Our rules are specific and strict:

we import only items we can establish as having disappeared from their own day—treasure buried by someone who died without divulging his secret, for example, or something mentioned in contemporary annals as having been lost without trace. This rule is of course not entirely reliable, since we cannot be sure that some of these 'lost' items were not in fact removed by future intervention. However, we must trust in the divine plan for the universe." He gave a skeletal smile.

"The removal of something like this mask," Don Miguel ventured, "must inevitably have dangerous consequences...?" He gestured towards it. "The mass alone is enormous!"

"Oh, it may turn out that the mask is recorded as having been melted down, so that the loss of simple mass—even in the form of gold—could pass unnoticed. I'm praying to that end, for it would offer the simplest solution. What is truly frightening is the psychological aspect of the matter. Such a mask as this would not have been a mere ornament, but the object of pagan veneration, known to thousands of people in its own time. It is not interference with things, or even with human beings, but with the development of *ideas* which implies the greatest potential alteration of history. You follow me?"

"I think so," Don Miguel muttered, feeling chilled to the marrow by the calm unemotional words.

"Suppose we find its loss recorded, Father?" the Prince interjected. "Does that mean we can keep it after all?"

The Jesuit shrugged. "As yet, I dare not say. We would then have to determine whether history had in fact been changed by interference, and if so whether truth demanded restitution of the former state of affairs."

The smile with which he accompanied the remark was actually quite pleasant, but it was no more comforting to Don

Miguel than the grin of a death's-head. He said, "Father, I'm glad I'm involved on the practical side of the Society. My mind boggles at the depth of these philosophical problems."

"You may not be so pleased tomorrow," rumbled the Prince. "We're charging you with a problem which is deep enough in its own way." He swept the others with an inquiring glance, and received confirmatory nods. "You are to discover the origin in our time of this mask, and identify the stranger Higgins bought it from. And you have two weeks in which to complete the task."

Two weeks! Dismayed, Don Miguel said, "Sir, I—I feel unworthy of such a . . ."

The Prince snorted. "Worthy or unworthy, Navarro, you opened up the case. We're telling you to close it as well!"

SIX

In its way the assignment was a signal honour—if the General Officers were as concerned as Father Ramón had indicated about illicit time-travellers and their perilous souvenirs, they would never charge someone they didn't trust with carrying it out.

But it was also a terrifying burden, and the more Don Miguel reflected on it, the more qualms he felt.

He was, as he had said, still under thirty; his time licence was little more than four years old, and his experience of fieldwork had been confined to a mere five trips, from the last of which he had returned bearing the scar of that Macedonian battle which would mark his face until he died, because an extratemporal infection had poisoned it and the medicines of the Society's doctors had proved impotent to destroy the germ. (They had found out how to cure the sufferers, but that was after his own wound had cicatrised.)

Nonetheless, his sense of duty might have carried him to the task with relative equanimity, had it not been for the fearful news Father Ramón had imparted to him at the meeting. Thirty Licentiates of the Society suspected of taking bribes? It was hardly believable! To Don Miguel timework had something of the air of a sacred trust; one of his lifelong heroes had always been the Society's founder, Borromeo, whose epochal discovery in 1892 had filled him with such apprehension that he did not rest easy until there was Papal supervision of all time apparatus and organisations existed to control its use. In the Empire, he had founded the Society of Time, while in the Confederacy of the East an analogous body called the Temporal College had been established under the Treaty of Prague.

No sane man, Don Miguel had always thought, would question the need to regulate time-travel. But now he wondered how much of the rigorously policed administration he was accustomed to derived from common sense, and how much from crude raw fear, which familiarity could erode with the passage of time.

There was no shortage of rational justifications for the Society's rule confining time-travel to observation without interference; for example, it had often been pointed out that if such a rule were not made and kept time-travellers from the future, visiting what to them was the past, would be noticed in the here-and-now. They had not been—therefore the rule was being obeyed.

Given almost a century of routine time-travel, though, it was scarcely to be marvelled at if that element of caution which was founded on fear rather than rational judgement were to fade. People were likely to grow blasé about anything routine, even when not merely their lives but the very history which led up to them depended on non-interference.

And if the rule were broken wholesale . . .

Don Miguel had inchoate visions of vast areas of time being swept into some unimaginable vacuum, into the formlessness of absolute not-being. Contemplating the consequences made his head ache. Like any other Licentiate, he had struggled through a full three-year course in the theory of time-travel on top of a regular university education—for him, the latter had included history, mathematics and natural philosophy—in order to graduate from Probationer to Licentiate status. He had cracked his skull over the relationship between familiar substantive time, in which one measured out one's daily life, and hard-to-grasp durative time in which one experienced events during a time-journey, and he had written his graduation thesis on the subject of so-called hypertime, the barrier which prevented a time-traveller returning from the past from going any further futurewards than the moment "then" reached by the apparatus which had launched him.

But all these were as nothing compared to the hypothetical complexities of speculative time, in which events would be otherwise than as history recounted.

What reality would take the place of his own if someone really smashed the non-interference rule to bits? Would Jorque be York; would an English monarch sit the Imperial throne? Would a Mohawk prince rule New Castile and call his subjects braves and squaws? Would there—could there—be a world in which men travelled into space instead of through time, by some undreamed-of miracle of propulsion?

But pondering such incredible speculations was not to Don Miguel's pragmatic taste. After doing his best to discipline his mind into logical analysis of the implications, he decided he was better employed in action than in mentation, and accordingly set off for another interview with the merchant, Higgins.

The guards on the door of Higgins's cell inspected his commission before admitting him; on discovering that it was over the Prince's own seal, they gave way with much bowing and scraping. Passing the door, he found himself in a room which—by prison standards—was spacious, though poorly lit and not at all well ventilated.

In the centre Higgins sat lolling on a chair, his head on one shoulder, his mouth ajar. He was fastened down with leather straps. At a table facing him were two inquisitors charged with his interrogation, conferring in low tones. Their expressions were anxious and they frowned continually. Upon Don Miguel's entrance they rose to greet him.

"How goes it?" demanded Don Miguel, and they exchanged glaces.

"Badly," said the taller of the two at last. "We greatly fear he may have been bewitched."

For a second Don Miguel wondered if the remark was meant for a joke. When he realised it was not, his heart sank. Was it not bad enough to have tangled with the paradoxes of temporal interference—must he now confront the shady, seldom-acknowledged borderline universe of enchantment?

Keeping his self-control with some effort, he said, "How so?"

"We have used all means that are lawful to unlock his tongue," the shorter inquisitor said. "We have employed liquors of divers kinds and we have used mirrors and pendulums. Since he is not convicted of any offence as yet we are forbidden to try more drastic methods. So far, all we have established is that while he remembers purchasing the mask he cannot recall the face of the man who sold it, nor his name, nor any clue to his identity."

Don Miguel felt a pang of dismay. He had hoped that at least one fresh clue would emerge from this interrogation. He said, "Does that mean we still have nothing concrete except the date of the deal?"

"I'm afraid so," the shorter inquisitor sighed. "And he gave us that truthfully of his own free will. Have you, though, inquired of the authorities in Jorque concerning the travellers who registered with them on or about that date?"

"Of course, but . . ." Don Miguel shrugged. "The person who brought the mask for sale has not been traced. No doubt he ignored the requirements of the law."

"The justification of the law lies in men's obedience thereof," said the taller inquisitor in sententious tones. It was not an observation which struck Don Miguel as adding very much to the discussion.

He said, "Well, at least you can tell me what kind of enchantment this villain might have used."

"There are many possibilities. One imagines a drug of some sort, to dull the will. Or he may have constrained Higgins to look at some bright spot—perhaps a reflection on the mask itself—and then soothed him to oblivion with gentle words."

"This kind of thing is possible?" Don Miguel demanded.

"Why, surely sir, Though we prefer that the fact should not be noised around; you'll understand that these are the techniques we use ourselves in inquisition, and it would be fatal if people were forewarned about them."

Don Miguel shook his head in wonder. He found all this barely credible; however, the inquisitors were experts in their own field, and he was compelled to take their word.

"Do you still hold out any hope of further progress?" he ventured.

"Very little, sir. Very little indeed—though of course we shall continue to try."

If the interrogation of Higgins had reached a dead end, the only thing to do was to head back to Jorque and continue his investigations on the spot where the mask had turned up. Accordingly, he left Londres that same evening by fast coach, and passed a miserably uncomfortable night in wishing that someone would hit on a safe means of adapting time apparatus to ordinary land-travel. In extreme emergencies, theory suggested, it could in fact be used for such a purpose, by employing the spatial displacement factor; it was not, however, judged safe to turn this notion into practice, because the travellers must inevitably arrive a small fraction of a second before leaving their starting-points, and the effects of this phenomenon were inherently unpredictable.

Therefore there were coaches, with horses to drag them along . . . and maybe nothing more was needed than better roads, complained Don Miguel's tortured bones as he made his way after a hasty breakfast from the staging-inn to the Jorque office of the Society, a great house set in spacious grounds not far from the cathedral.

Here he was received by an old-young man with a pale face and high, hesitant voice whose eyes fastened greedily on the Prince's seal at the foot of Don Miguel's commission. He was probably a failed Licentiate, Don Miguel diagnosed from his manner and his tone.

"We have much discussed the problem which you are come to look into," said the fellow fawningly, having introduced himself as Don Pedro Diaz. "We are all impressed with the way you saw straight to its heart."

Don Miguel was in no mood for hollow flattery. He

countered brusquely, "It was no more than anyone of intelligence fit to grace the Society must necessarily have deduced! As yet, moreover, the heart of the matter still eludes me. Since my departure for Londres, have you found out anything further concerning the stranger who's alleged to have brought the mask for sale?"

The other looked disconcerted. "Why, we were not told to do so," he objected. "Was it not enough to have arrested the merchant Higgins and his clerks?"

Sometimes Don Miguel found himself wondering how it was that almost a century had safely passed since Borromeo turned time-travel loose in this imperfect world. Right now he was tempted to draw his sword on this idiot and inscribe his hide with a message to be memorised concerning the responsibilities of the Society. However, he controlled himself.

"It was not enough," he said shortly. "If that's all you can offer me, though, I'll make a start with it. Where are these clerks you referred to?"

"At once!" Don Pedro exclaimed. "I'll take you to see them myself!"

But the clerks were even less helpful than Higgins had been. Their story, to the truth of which the local inquisitors testified, was that their master had conducted both the purchase and the later sale of the mask himself, as he often did when the other party involved was of noble status. That, Don Miguel had to concede, was logical enough—he could imagine any nobleman compelled to dispose of family heirlooms and replenish a shrinking coffer wanting to treat in confidence with a discreet merchant, and he already knew that Higgins's reputation for discretion had brought him many such transactions.

The clerks maintained stoutly that they had been unaware

of the mask's existence until their master was arrested, and their story—like Higgins's own—had so far defied the best efforts of the inquisitors to undermine it.

Sighing, Don Miguel left the cell in which they were incarcerated and headed back through the fine grounds of the Society's office. Having gone some distance with Don Pedro silent at his side, he suddenly spoke up.

"This market, now, where the mask was sold to Don Arcimboldo—it's outside the city wall, is it not?"

"Indeed it is, sir," Don Pedro answered. "Save for freemen of Jorque, who seldom engage in trade, no one may buy or sell goods within the wall; there was a by-law passed in the last years of last century. Thus the custom arose of going beyond the walls to trade, and now indeed the market district has grown almost into a new city of itself."

"Good. I want to inspect this market. Call me a coach and let's be gone."

"With pleasure, sir," declared Don Pedro fervently.

While they were waiting before the Society's office for the vehicle to arrive, Don Miguel turned to the other subject he was currently interested in.

"Tell me, Don Pedro, what do you know about Don Arcimboldo Ruiz? Is he a prominent figure here in Jorque?"

"He's . . ." Don Pedro hesitated oddly. "He's of a prominent family in the north."

Don Miguel nodded. "As to him personally, though?" he prompted.

"I can tell you rather little, I'm afraid. I do know he's inherited large estates over the Scottish border, but prefers to live in Jorque for the sake of our social life. I also know he's highly regarded as a collector of Saxon and Irish antiques— men speak of him as having expert knowledge on that subject.

Beyond that . . ." He concluded with a shrug.

Of course, this was no news to Don Miguel; Don Arcimboldo had come straight out and said he collected antiques, but New World artefacts were not his speciality. His verdict on the personality of the Marquesa had indicated a healthy cynicism, and implied that if he had had any cause to suspect Higgins of selling him contraband he would have taken steps to protect himself. He would hardly have given such a splendid gift to the Marquesa, knowing its existence would be public knowledge within the day, had he feared it was an unlicensed import. Either he would not have bought it, or he would have kept it secretly for his own collection. Yes, the argument was colourable.

And yet . . .

Don Miguel's train of thought was interrupted by the arrival of the coach Don Pedro had called for. But the tiny crease of puzzlement which had developed between his eyebrows remained there throughout the coach-ride.

They called the place a "market"; in fact, as Don Pedro had forewarned him, it had grown until it was almost a city in its own right. Wide roads, well paved, traversed it and separated the plots of ground leased to various traders, on which had been erected booths backed by solid stone warehouses. During the day goods were brought forth from the latter and displayed under awnings, or by the most prosperous merchants in little huts sided with glass, while brawny slaves guarded them with clubs. At night they would be taken back into the warehouses and firmly secured against robbers.

Instructing Don Pedro to dismiss the coach for an hour, Don Miguel set forth on foot for a tour of the market. He paused apparently at random—to test the quality of nutmegs

at a spicer's, to feel some splendid Eastern brocades in a
draper's, to examine a set of candlesticks in a silversmith's—
and as he did so he asked casual-seeming questions of the
staff. Somehow, to Don Pedro's increasingly obvious admiration, he contrived to introduce into each such conversation the names of Higgins and Don Arcimboldo.

The expiry of the hour saw them emerging from a book-
binder's, where gold-leaf glittered on fine calf bindings and
the air was rich with the scent of leather and size, and with
that Don Pedro's patience ran dry.

"Sir!" he exclaimed. "The subtlety of your inquiries has
amazed me—truly it has!"

"Subtlety?" Don Miguel echoed with a scowl, striding in
the direction of the spot where they were to rejoin their coach.
Their course was taking them through the heart of the
market, and at this noontide juncture the place was crowded.
Retainers from noble families, bearing conspicuous crests,
kept shoving their way through with arrogance, a fact which
greatly annoyed Don Pedro but which Don Miguel put up
with stoically. They could have cleared a path for themselves
by merely mentioning the name of the Society, let alone
displaying its arms—the scythe and hourglass which Borromeo
had personally chosen for its insignia—but it was a bad time
to draw attention to themselves.

"Subtlety?" he said again, and added a savage chuckle.
"Well, if it's subtle to fail completely in trying to answer an
all-important question, I'll agree . . . Don't bother me for a
moment, if you please! I'm desperately struggling to think!"

Embarrassed, Don Pedro shut his mouth like a rat-trap,
and did not utter another word apart from inviting Don
Miguel to precede him into the coach, until the latter spoke
again nearly halfway back to the Society's office.

"Don Pedro! A word of advice from you!"

"You do me much honour," Don Pedro said nervously. "I trust I can provide what you want."

"Well, I can't figure it out for myself. You have a go. Imagine you were in Don Arcimboldo's place, heir to lands in Scotland and a highly respected collector of antiques: why would you give a very rare and costly mask of solid gold to a lady who is—to be blunt—far past the age of courtship?"

Don Pedro's eyes widened. For a long moment he said nothing; then finally he ventured, "Well, perhaps from motives of simple friendship . . . ?"

What Don Arcimboldo had said about the Marquesa during her party ruled out that possibility, in Don Miguel's view. He dismissed the suggestion with a wave of his hand, not bothering to explain why.

"Another reason?" he invited.

"Well . . ." Don Pedro swallowed enormously. "Far be it from me to impute anything to someone as respected as Don Arcimboldo, but . . . Perhaps one might assume he stood to gain by his action?"

"I'm very much afraid one might. Don Pedro, instruct your coachman to detour by way of Higgins's residence in the town. I trust you're not in a great hurry for your lunch—this may take a little time."

In fact, the stop at Higgins's home lasted a mere twenty minutes, but when he came away Don Miguel was frowning like thunderclouds and responded to Don Pedro's attempts at conversation only with frigid grunts.

Then, on their return to the Society's office, he found a message awaiting him, received by semaphore telegraph from Londres a few minutes before. It was a report from Red Bear's field-teams, informing him that the gold mask was almost certainly the work of a celebrated Aztec goldsmith called Nezahualcoyotl—Hungry Dog. And that established its origin in the middle fifteenth century, most likely in the great town of Texcoco.

Another puzzle for him! If the mask was the work of such a famous craftsman that Red Bear's staff could identify it so positively, why should a collector of art-objects *give* it away, even if he didn't want it for his own collection? Surely the logical thing would be to sell it, and use the proceeds to enlarge . . .

A great light suddenly broke in on Don Miguel. Facts clicked together in his mind and formed a pattern, a pattern which made sound sense. He slammed fist into palm and rounded on Don Pedro.

"I see it! And yet I do not see it! If—Don Pedro, send speedily to the Holy Office here in Jorque and ask for a skilled inquisitor to attend me and answer certain questions. Then have a coach reserved for me, and be sure the driver knows the way to the home of Don Arcimboldo, for I purpose to call on him tonight."

"It shall be done," promised Don Pedro, and hurried away.

Don Miguel conversed lengthily with the inquisitor who came in answer to his request, in private and alone. When they parted it was near dark, yet he refused Don Pedro's invitation to stay and take a bite to eat. Instead, he buckled on his sword, threw a cloak about him, and headed into the dusk as though fiends were hot on his heels.

SEVEN

Don Arcimboldo's town house in Jorque, though far from
new, was handsome and spacious and stood in extensive
grounds. The interior bespoke luxury and good taste. The
same raw materials that Don Miguel had encountered at the
Marquesa's—creeping plants trained on sculptured artificial
boughs, hothouse flowers that turned the rooms into miniature gardens, exquisite tiling and panelling and many price-
less antique ornaments—had been employed here, but by
someone with far superior judgement.

It seemed a shame, Don Miguel felt, to come here for the
first time on such an errand. But, weighted down with his
burden of suspicion, he hardened his heart.

The major-domo who had admitted him presented his
master's apologies, saying that he was at dinner but would
shortly be finished and would wait on his distinguished guest;
in the meantime, would Don Miguel be so kind as to occupy

himself in the library?

Don Miguel would. Wine was brought for him by a Guinea-girl—exceptionally beautiful, hence either very expensive or born into the service of the family, for slaves were prohibitively costly nowadays—who poured him his first glass and offered it with a curtsey, then retired to sit in the darkest corner among the bookcases, her white eyes and white teeth glimmering in the shadow.

Glass in hand, Don Miguel wandered absently around the room. It was not merely a library, despite its name. It was almost a museum, and shelf after shelf contained ornaments and curios. The majority of them were, as he had been led to expect, of Saxon, Norse and Irish origin; there were, however, many Moorish and Oriental items, in gold and silver and turquoise and even jade.

He nodded in bitter satisfaction and shifted his attention to the books, which proved that Don Arcimboldo enjoyed truly catholic—but definitely not Catholic—taste. There was one case which would probably have sent Father Peabody into hysterics . . . or perhaps not. Reconsidering the idea, Don Miguel concluded that his long acquaintance with the Marquesa had probably cured the priest of his tendency to hysteria. Nonetheless, the majority of these volumes were on the Index, and not by any means all for simple heresy.

He selected a finely illustrated edition of the *Satyricon* of Petronius Arbiter to pass the time until Don Arcimboldo should enter, and settled himself in a superb leather chair, very comfortable and tooled all over with gilt.

When at length the host did appear, he was full of apologies for making Don Miguel wait. But Don Miguel waved his protestations aside.

"I should have sent ahead to say you must expect me," he

declared. "But I've not regretted the time I've spent browsing here. It's given me excellent insight into your tastes as a collector, both of curios and of books."

Don Arcimboldo dropped into a chair that was the twin of Don Miguel's and snapped his fingers for the Guinea-girl to fetch him wine. "What taste I have, to be candid, is dictated by little more than the desire to surround myself with beautiful objects. However, if my self-indulgence affords pleasure for others, I see no reason to deny it." He gave a soft chuckle and sipped his drink.

"Incontestably you have a remarkable collection," said Don Miguel. "Tell me, did you acquire all of these things here in Jorque?"

"Very many of them, including most of the best. Our great market—you've seen it, yes?—is a splendid hunting-ground for rarities. As a matter of fact, I bought most of the gold and silver from Higgins, who's a specialist in that area. I wonder: have you any news of him?"

"He sticks to his unconvincing story of having acquired the Aztec mask from a stranger."

"Poor fellow!" Don Arcimboldo murmured. "I wonder what can have possessed him!"

There was a pause, during which the Guinea-girl came to see whether their glasses needed replenishing. Having spilled a symbolic drop into each, she would have returned to her corner, but her employer dismissed her from the room.

"An interesting choice of phrase," Don Miguel said, as soon as the door had closed behind the slave.

Don Arcimboldo blinked at him. "I don't think I quite ...?"

"Your saying you don't know what *possessed* Higgins," Don Miguel amplified, turning his wineglass between his fingers. "The term is almost too literal, you know. The inquisitors believe him to have been enchanted."

"Villainous!" Don Arcimboldo exclaimed. "What a foul trick to play on an honourable tradesman!"

"Yes," Don Miguel agreed, and once more there was a short silence.

"By the way," Don Arcimboldo resumed at length, "there's something I suppose I should have said to you in Londres."

Don Miguel inclined his head and looked politely alert.

"I hold no grudge against you for acting as you did in this matter. Of course not. I fully understand how seriously any question of temporal contraband must be regarded."

"I'm pleased to hear it," Don Miguel murmured. "Some people seem to treat the dangers over-lightly."

"I'd never do so! Oh, I'm hardly one to talk, of course—I confess I should have made inquiries about the mask, in view of its perfect condition. But as you know that's not my speciality . . . Tell me, though, if you're free to do so: how was it that the mask got brought to the present? Surely only Licentiates are permitted to travel in time, and one can hardly imagine a Licentiate being corruptible!"

"It would appear," Don Miguel said after a moment's debate with himself, "that certain—ah—*outsiders* have contrived to grease the necessary palms and get taken on visits to the past. Doubtless one of them brought the mask back."

"Terrible!" Don Arcimboldo widened his eyes. "And yet . . Well, I could find it in my heart to envy such outsiders." He grinned with engaging frankness. "You wouldn't appreciate the urge which someone like myself feels to walk among the people to whom the rare and beautiful objects I collect were modern—virtually commonplace! Do you suppose, Don Miguel, the day will come when private applicants, properly indoctrinated against the risk of interfering with the past, will be permitted to share the marvel of time-travel?"

"If you're wondering whether I am one of the Licentiates whose palm is open to being greased," said Don Miguel coldly, "I assure you I am not."

"No—no, of course not!" Distressed, Don Arcimboldo half-rose. "I had no intention of implying . . ."

"Then shall we change the subject?" Don Miguel deliberately exploited the presumptive insult to let an acid tone enter his voice. "Shall we speak of your collection? Shall we for example discuss the fact that it contains not merely your Saxon and Irish and Norse antiques, but also Moorish, Oriental, and other items I fail to recognise?"

At a loss, Don Arcimboldo said, "Why, certainly it does, but—"

"In short, your taste is more eclectic than I was led to believe." Don Miguel set his glass aside, not looking at the other man directly. "Which makes it surprising that you did not keep the Aztec mask, having bought it. Tell me, why did you give it to the Marquesa, Don Arcimboldo?"

His host's face darkened. "It is unseemly to pry into such personal matters!"

"I have no choice. I have a commission to fulfil, under the orders of the Prince of New Castile."

"Your behaviour is ungracious and unmannerly nonetheless! However, I will answer—if you'll give me good grounds for requiring the information."

Don Miguel rose from his chair and walked, glass in hand, towards a display of fine Saxon torcs and belt-buckles in hammered gold, many of the latter set with garnets. Not looking in Don Arcimboldo's direction, he said, "You must have had a reason for adding so hugely to your debt to

Higgins. It can hardly have been a moment's whim which led you almost to double your already long-outstanding obligations."

There was no immediate reply. When Don Miguel turned away from the antiques he was admiring, he found that Don Arcimboldo had drawn a delicately wrought silver chain from a pouch at his belt, with a little pendant on the bottom of some sort of glittering crystal, and was letting it swing from his fingers as though suddenly very nervous.

"I suppose you took possession of Higgins's records," he muttered eventually. "But the cold figures give a misleading impression, I assure you. There was no reason for him to doubt my credit. After all, I'm far from being a poor man."

"Indeed?" said Don Miguel glacially.

"What do you mean?" Don Arcimboldo flushed and bridled, though the swinging chain did not vary its pendulum-like motion. "Do you think that this place around you is the home of a pauper?"

"Yes."

The single sharp word seemed to drain much of the spirit out of Don Arcimboldo. He gave a sigh. "I yield, I yield . . . There is a grain of truth in what you say, for of late my estates in Scotland have not provided me with as much as they used to. Accordingly I will tell you why I gave the mask to the Marquesa. I hoped that she would loan me a sum to rescue me from my temporary—temporary!—difficulties."

The chain went on swinging. There was silence. Don Miguel allowed the silence to stretch. And, after a little while, Don Arcimboldo's self-possession began to fray. He looked first puzzled, then alarmed. When the alarm was acute enough, Don Miguel spoke out.

"It's no use. Don Arcimboldo! Before coming here I spent a

long while in conversation with an inquisitor who is expert in matters of the mind. I have taken an antidote to the sort of drug you gave me in this very good wine. So you cannot lull my brain with your swinging crystal and wheedle me into forgetfulness—as you served Higgins!"

The last phrase cracked like the lash of a whip. Don Arcimboldo let fall his hands; white-faced he whimpered, "I swear I do not understand!"

"Your oath is false. You understand me well. What has happened went like this. The temptation to join fortunate outsiders who have voyaged illegally into the past grew too strong for you to resist, but in order to bribe the corrupt Licentiate who made your journey possible you were compelled to overspend your income. Consequently you ran up a debt with Higgins—an undignified situation! Doubtless he pestered you for his money, and you feared he might warn the other merchants in the market that you were defaulting on a bill. Presumably—for you are not at bottom a stupid man— your original intention in smuggling back the splendid Aztec mask was merely to keep it in secret and gloat over it by yourself. When Higgins became a nuisance, I think you must have considered offering it to him in settlement, and then rejected the idea, knowing his reputation for caution and his habit of checking that the extratemporal objects he was offered had been licensed by my Society. So you hit on a subtler way out of your corner. You deluded him into believing he had bought the mask from someone else.

"Small wonder he cannot tell the inquisitors from whom! How can one remember a person who did not exist? But you did not manage to get at his clerks, did you? I've spoken to them, and even the clerk who keeps Higgins's stock-list had no record of the mask.

"Oh, possibly this was intended to lend colour to the hoped-for outcome, the imprisonment of Higgins for trading in temporal contraband. In jail he could scarcely continue to dun you for his money! I deduce this from your action in giving the mask to the Marquesa, who could be relied upon to boast about it within days and draw the attention of someone like myself who would recognise the illegality of its presence here. Whereupon you would play the innocent dupe, and let Higgins suffer the rigours of the law.

"You acted your role well. Indeed, until you drew that chain from your pouch I still half-doubted my own con- clusions. But the inquisitor I talked to this afternoon warned me about such tricks, and now I'm convinced beyond a doubt."

Don Arcimboldo cast the silver chain violently to the floor. "It's a pack of lies!" he shouted. "This nonsense will never convince anyone but a fool like you!"

"I'm prepared to take that risk," Don Miguel said stonily. He slid his sword from its scabbard and presented its point to the other's chest. "Don Arcimboldo Ruiz, by the authority in me vested of the Society of Time I arrest you on charges of temporal contraband and desire you to go with me to face trial. You may have met one corrupt Licentiate, Don Arcimboldo—but learn from this that some of us take our rules seriously. After all, we are meddling with the very fabric of the universe."

EIGHT

The vacant space between the crystal pillars hummed
faintly; those present in the hall shifted on their chairs, wiping
their faces now and then. It was always warm in the neigh-
bourhood of the pillars when a traveller was about to return
from a voyage into time.

The Prince of New Castile seemed worse affected by the
heat than were his colleagues, and grunted and muttered to
himself. Abruptly he could not stand it any longer, and
snapped his fingers at an attentive aide nearby.

"Wine!" he barked. "The heat is terrible!"

"Yes, your highness," said the aide alertly. "And for the
Gerneral Officers as well?"

Red Bear moved his long Indian face once in a gesture of
acceptance, but Father Ramón did not stir. After a pause, the
Prince waved at the aide to hurry up.

"Think you it is well done, Father?" he snapped.

Father Ramón seemed to come back to the present from a private voyage into the elsewhen. He sketched a brief smile, turning to the Prince.

"As well done as we may do," he parried. "At least we know that the golden mask is being restored; whether the restoration itself was wise, we can only guess."

Red Bear snorted. "If you had doubts about the wisdom of putting the thing back, why give me so much trouble over it?"

"We must always doubt our own wisdom," said Father Ramón peaceably. He raised a hand towards the crystal pillars. "I think the moment is at hand—the humming grows louder."

The technicians on duty around the time-hall had tensed to their positions. Now, suddenly, there was a clap like thunder and a smell of raw heat, and in the space between the pillars a shape appeared: a curious shape of iron and silver bars, that seemed to glow for a moment as energy washed out of their substance in the process of their rotation back to normal dimensionality.

In the middle of the frame, a man's form was seen to collapse.

Father Ramón jerked to his feet. "Be swift!" he ordered the technicians. "Help him—come on, move!"

The technicians darted forward, some to dismantle the frame of metal bars, others to help Don Miguel to his feet and lead him to a couch that stood waiting. Slaves hastened to fetch restoratives and basins of clean warm water.

A bare half-hour had elapsed in the hall since the moment they had dispatched their emissary to the past. But it was plain that for him much time had gone by. His skin was burnt by sun to the colour of leather, and his eyes were red and inflamed with dust. The General Officers gathered anxiously about his couch, wondering how gravely he had suffered.

Not especially, it transpired. For, having accepted a sip or two of stimulating cordial, he brushed aside further attentions and managed to sit up. He passed his tongue over sun-chapped lips and spoke in a thick slow voice.

"It is done," he said, and looked about him as though not yet convinced of his return to the familiar world. His mind was still whirling with the memory of the great city of Texcoco burning in tropic daylight, as his body was still clad only in the breech-clout of an Indian of that time. The slaves had begun to wash away the painted symbols from his cheeks, but had completed only half their task; the division of his face summed up the way he was still poised between two realities.

The General Officers breathed a sigh of relief. Red Bear said harshly, "You are certain?"

"Absolutely. I found the workshop of Hungry Dog without trouble, at the very time he was working on the mask. When it was complete, it waited in his house for the festival at which it was to be dedicated with sacrifices to the great god Tez-catlipoca. I contrived to see it on a number of occasions prior to the date of the festival. And the last day before, a man came into the shop and stole the mask."

"Was it Don Arcimboldo?" demanded the Prince.

"Presumably. Perhaps."

"Aren't you certain?" The Prince leaned forward angrily, but Father Ramón laid a hand restrainingly on his arm.

"Our brother Navarro has done well," he said.

"How so, if he cannot prove who the thief was?" the Prince countered, blinking.

"Why, he had at all costs to avoid the risk of being seen by Don Arcimboldo. Had they met, Don Arcimboldo might have recognised him when they met at the Marquesa's. This did not happen. Therefore it was correct not to confront him."

"So I reasoned," said Don Miguel, laying his head wearily in his hands. "Accordingly, when I saw the mask was gone, I simply replaced it—I mean I replaced it with the version I'd brought from now. I stayed long enough to ensure that it was dedicated at the festival as planned, and . . . here I am."

The Prince grunted. "It's all in order now, you think, Father Ramón?"

"As far as we can tell."

"Good! Then I must go back to New Castile. Had it not been for this delay I'd planned to leave Londres days ago. Red Bear, I charge you with attending to the rest of the details. Good day!"

He gave curt nods to his colleagues and departed from the time-hall with cloak flying and aides trotting at his heels. After a thoughtful pause, Red Bear moved away from Don Miguel's couch to supervise the dismantling of the time apparatus, and Father Ramón remained alone.

"How do you feel, my son?" he asked eventually.

"I begin to recover," said Don Miguel, and accepted another sip of the cordial. "My hurts are more in my mind than in my body. I was witness to a sacrifice to Tezcatlipoca less than a day ago, and I still feel nauseated."

"Understandably," the Jesuit said with sympathy.

Don Miguel sat up on the couch with his arms linked around his shins and set his chin on his knees, staring into nowhere. After a pause he said, "You know, Father, it sometimes makes me wonder what blindness we also may be guilty of."

"Explain further," the Jesuit invited.

"Well . . . Well, what I mean is this. I recall the Marquesa saying to me how much she admires the goldwork and featherwork of the Aztecs, and it's true: their artistry was magnificent. Yet for all their art, their masonry, their social discipline, the people I've just been among were savages, habituated to sacrificing men by the score in the most cruel manner. For all that they understood the motion of the stars and planets, they never used the wheel except to move children's toy animals. In some ways, unquestionably, we're superior. And yet we may have our blind spots too. Although Borromeo showed us how we might rotate the dimensions of substances so that the world becomes flat and we can voyage back into time, although we live in an orderly world rid of much of the horror of war—nonetheless, one cannot but wonder whether we too are wasting on children's toys marvels that later ages will put to use."

"Yes," said Father Ramón, following with his eyes the movement of the technicians taking apart the framework of iron and silver. And then he repeated more slowly, "Ye-es . . ."

"What is perhaps worse still," continued Don Miguel, "is the knowledge that we—unworthy as we are—have the power to re-shape history! So far we have managed to confine that power to a nucleus of reliable individuals. But out of a thousand or so Licentiates, if thirty have already proved corruptible—why, our greed and carelessness could wreck history back to the moment of Creation!"

Father Ramón seemed to draw himself together inside his habit. He said, "We are gifted with free will, my son. It is unquestionably a very heavy burden."

Suddenly incredulous, Don Miguel twisted around on the couch and stared at him. "But . . . ! Father, how could this never have occurred to me before? With time-travel, would it not be possible for agents of evil to plot journeys back into time, with the intention of undoing the good consequences of the acts of others? Would it not even be possible for such persons to deliberately corrupt the great men of the past?"

"You are astute," said Father Ramón after a second's debate with himself. "It has indeed been conjectured that the influence of evil which we discern in our history may be the working out of just such interference as you suggest. Some theorists have even argued that the fall of the angels hurled from heaven may have been a plunge through time, rather than through space. But this is the deepest of all theological questions today."

It occurred to Don Miguel that he ought perhaps to be surprised at carrying on this casual conversation with one of the august General Officers of the Society, especially with this Jesuit whose reputation was that of an aloof philosopher inhabiting the rarefied regions of advanced metaphysics. Yet he seemed singularly approachable—far more so than, say, Red Bear.

He ventured, "I myself do not see how such a question could be answered at all."

"You mean the question as to whether the good results of human actions could be wiped out by temporal interference? Good, of course, cannot be destroyed, and it is heretical to maintain that it can."

The edge of reproof on the Jesuit's voice cut Don Miguel's self-assurance to ribbons. He said humbly, "In that case it was foolish of me to voice my speculation."

"Paradoxically, it was the reverse of foolish. It showed rather unusual insight." Father Ramón rose, seeming to reach a decision. "When you are rested, my son, visit me in my private office. I think you deserve some information you have not yet been given."

NINE

Father Ramón's office was perfectly bare; there was no ornament bar an ivory crucifix and a candle, not even the usual portrait of St. Ignatius. It contained only bookcases, a desk and two chairs, one hard, one soft. The Jesuit was himself sitting in the hard one when Don Miguel entered, and indicated that the other was for his visitor. Sitting down uncertainly, Don Miguel wondered what information he was to be made privy to.

Father Ramón offered him tobacco and a pipe, which he refused, and then leaned back, putting his fingertips together.

"Consider what makes an act of free will free," he said.

The suddenness of the question took Don Miguel aback. He muttered a confused answer which Father Ramón ignored.

"No, it consists in this: that all the possible outcomes be fulfilled."

"*What?*"

"Precisely that. If there is free will—and we hold *a priori* that there is—all opportunities for decision must conclude in just so many ways as there are alternatives. Thus to kill and not to kill and merely to wound more or less severely—*all* these must follow upon a choice between them."

"But I don't understand! There—there is no *room* for that to be true!"

"No?" The other sketched his habitual faint smile. "Then approach it from a concrete instance. You go into the past. You abstract a crucial object—shall we say a bullet from a gun aimed by an assassin at a king? A king may change history by living or dying. Would you thereupon return to the same present as the one you left?"

"No, of course not," said Don Miguel, and heard his voice shaking.

"But knowledge is indestructible, isn't it? The knowledge, for example, of how to construct time apparatus! So is there any reason why, from that alternative historical outcome, you shouldn't return to replace the bullet? The king dies—*again*, so to speak. And the present to which you return after restoring the *status quo* . . . is the original present."

"Father, you are telling me that this kind of thing has already been done?"

"We have been doing it for nearly forty years."

"But this is far more dangerous than what's been done by the corrupt Licentiates!" Don Miguel cried, feeling the universe reel around him. It was known to everyone in the Society, and suspected by a few outsiders, that its upper echelons were party to unshared secrets; the incumbent Pope, for example, at the inception of his reign was now customarily taken on a trip into the period of the ministry of Jesus himself, a zone of history completely banned to anyone else. But to have been assured that Jesus was a historical figment could hardly have been a more terrifying blow than what Father Ramón had just announced.

The Jesuit looked at him calmly.

"There is no corruption in this matter. There is only an honest desire to explore the works of our Creator, that we may the more completely comprehend His omnipotence. Would you condemn in the same breath a thief who stole away a valuable watch in order to dispose of it for gain, and a student of horology who took it in order to inspect and copy the mechanism, so that he might improve his own abilities?"

"Naturally not," agreed Don Miguel, his mind working furiously. "But—but if all this is true, it scarcely seems to matter whether we interfere or not! We ourselves may be only a fluid cohesion of possibilities, subject to change at the whim of someone who chooses not to obey the rule of non-interference."

"True," said Father Ramón stonily. "That is a logical consequence of there being free will; in His wisdom, God gave it not to an elect few, but to all mankind."

There was silence. Eventually Don Miguel said, "I suppose this might have been foreseen by anyone who troubled to work out in detail what kind of a future Borromeo's discovery opened up to us."

"We may give thanks that up to now few people have thought the matter through." Once more Father Ramón smiled. "Well, Don Miguel Navarro! How do you like the universe we live in?"

"I do not," said Don Miguel, and was at a loss to describe the sense of impermanence, volatility and changeability that the other's words had instilled in him.

"Nonetheless," said Father Ramón dryly, "this is how things are. Go now to Red Bear and report to him about your trip. And do not speak to anyone of what I've told you. For if this truth were to become known to those who are not ready for it—why, the sky would fall!"

When Don Miguel turned and walked to the door, he was surprised to find the floor still firm beneath his feet.

PART II

THE WORD NOT WRITTEN

ONE

The quatrocentennial year was dying in a blaze of glory. The winter weather had been kind, and New Year's Eve proved to be fine and mild, spiced with a wind whose nip was just enough to sharpen the step to briskness and put colour in the faces of the people. Bonfires had been lit at sunset in most of the main streets of Londres, and around them nut vendors, potato bakers and kebab men with their rapier-like skewers laden with alternate lumps of meat, kidney and onion cried their hot wares.

There had been a great mock battle on the Thames as dusk fell; natives and visitors had flocked in their thousands to witness the finest reconstruction ever presented of the battle between the all-conquering Armada and the gallant but pitiful English ships four hundred years ago—a re-enactment correct in every detail, thanks to the Society of Time.

Even so there were a few nationalist diehards in the crowd

who shouted objections to the display, maintaining that it was an insult to them and their ancestors. But most of the spectators answered with jeers, for they regarded themselves as subjects of the Empire regardless of what blood happened to flow in their veins: Spanish, English, French, Mohawk, Cherokee, Sioux . . . Soon enough the civil guards quieted the disturbance, and when a golden barge hove in sight bearing His Most Catholic Majesty Philip IX, *Rey y Imperador*, the loyal shout which greeted its appearance echoed across all Londres.

Smiling, bowing graciously from side to side, the King was rowed over the same water that shortly before had been blood-red with the fires of mock battle. Another barge followed, bearing the Prince Imperial, his Princess, and their children, and behind that again came the barge of the Prince of New Castile. The King's barge had sixteen oars a side; those of his sons had twelve, and at one of the oars sweated and cursed Don Miguel Navarro.

Whoever the blazes had thought up this delicate tribute to the royal family, he muttered to himself, ought by simple justice to have been pulling on the oars too. But it was fairly certain that he wouldn't be. He was probably simpering and dancing attendance on the King or the Prince Imperial.

Even though they were going with the stream, they were pulling against the last surge of the tide, and it called for real work to keep up with the King's barge, as it had eight more oars and was anyway less heavily laden. As a gesture of loyalty the idea was splendid; as a job it was abominable.

It was small consolation to reflect that this ceremony was the outcome of many months of behind-the-scenes intrigue at Court, and that precisely because he was Commander of the Society of Time the Prince of New Castile was going to play host this New Year's Eve to his father, elder brother, and a gang of foreign dignitaries, chief among them the Ambassador of the Confederacy of the East. Certainly it was a great and signal honour for the Society to have been chosen as the focus for the climax of the quatrocentennial year, but like a good many royal favours it had its drawbacks. Don Miguel struggled to ignore the ache in his arms and thought of the white elephants—sacred, hence obligatory to feed regardless of expense—which the Kings of Siam were reputed to give to subjects they intended to ruin.

He was in no mood for merrymaking anyway, what with the aftermath of the revelations Father Ramón had recently confided to him concerning the Society's exploration of unreal branches of history. With personal friends, in a place and among company of his own choosing, he might have passed a pleasant enough New Year's Eve, but as things stood he was compelled to follow up this chore on the river with a whole evening of acting as a host to all kinds of noble idiots in the Commander's palace at Greenwich. He could tell he was not alone among the younger Licentiates on the rowers' benches in thinking that this might prove unendurable.

Probably the crowds that watched the splendid water-procession from the embankments did not even imagine that anyone could object to being involved. Probably, when the spectacle was over, they dispersed sighing with envy, thinking of the magnificence of the royal reception and wishing they were prominent enough to be invited.

In bitter contrast Don Miguel and his companions sat hauling on their oars and envied the simple folk going off to spend New Year's Eve with their families or to join the revels which would make the streets noisy and bright until dawn.

"You'd think," he growled, selecting one of the many

discomforts that plagued him, "in a Prince's barge they'd at least pad the seats decently!"

His opposite number on the other side of the boat, another Licentiate of about his own age whose name was Don Felipe Basso, curled his lip. "It's clear you'd rather be anywhere else tonight, Miguel!" he answered in a low tone.

"Even Macedonia was better than this," Don Miguel agreed, invoking a reference to the field-trip into the age of Alexander the Great on which he had first made Don Felipe's acquaintance . . . and acquired the scar, which, while it merely twisted his smile, nowadays rendered his scowl positively ferocious.

"Don Miguel! Keep the time!"

From his post in the stern Don Arturo Cortés rapped the order in his shrill, acid voice. Seated in his most magnificent plum-coloured cloak and snow-white velvet breeches on a high-backed gilt and plush chair, he was making the most of his assignment as overseer of the amateur rowers. He was one of the senior Licentiates of the Society below General Officer rank; he had already commanded a number of expeditions into the past, and was widely tipped to succeed Red Bear as the Director of Fieldwork. Somehow he had acquired a General Officer's wand, to which he was not yet entitled, and was employing it as a baton to beat time for the oarsmen. Such a presumptuous gesture was typical of his overweening self-esteem.

Don Miguel bit back his answer—he was altogether too close alongside the tapestry pavilion in which the Prince was sitting to speak louder than a whisper without being overheard and perhaps ticked off—and leaned compliantly on his oar. But when Don Arturo's attention had wandered again, Don Felipe spoke softly.

"He doesn't seem to like you, Miguel!"

"Who—Don Arturo? That makes us even. I don't like him either."

"A little faster still!" rasped Don Arturo, rising now with his wand outstretched as though he were conductor of a band of music. "We're falling too far behind!"

By the time the barge was gentled in to the wharf near the Commander's palace, Don Miguel's buttocks were bruised, his hands were rubbed sore by the oar, and his temper was close to flashpoint. Face like thunder, he remained on his bench and watched Don Arturo with his usual officiousness directing the disembarkation of the Prince. With part of his mind, however, he was wondering whether out of sheer self-interest he ought to try and counter the dislike which Felipe had referred to. It was obvious where it had its source. Everyone seemed to think he had handled the recent affair of the contraband Aztec mask rather well—indeed, he was wearing tonight for the first time at any Society function the outward sign of the Commander's approval, the gem-encrusted collar and star of the Order of the Scythe and Hourglass which cynical old Borromeo himself had selected for the Society's emblem.

It crossed his mind that if he had played his cards right he might have used this new honour as a means of escaping duty on the rower's bench. But it was not in his nature to think of things like that at times when they might be helpful.

Don Arturo had a reputation for resenting any younger member of the Society who achieved too notable a success. The allegations were being borne out by the way he had treated Don Miguel lately. Simply for his own comfort Don Miguel reasoned, he would be well advised to play up a bit to Don Arturo.

But he wasn't going to start doing so this evening. Not after Don Arturo's performance aboard the barge.

"Are you going to sit here all night, Miguel?" Don Felipe said, clapping his friend on the shoulder. "Have you suddenly conceived a liking for that badly padded seat?"

Don Miguel sighed and roused himself, giving a rueful glance at his hands. "Why did I not think to bring leather-palmed gloves instead of my best white silk pair which the oar would have rubbed to shreds? Ah well, it's over, and I'm thankful. How long do you imagine it will be before we can find a drink?"

Companionably arm-in-arm with Felipe he made his way towards the gangplank.

The Prince was ashore by now. The wharf had been carpeted with purple, and a pathway of the same material led up over the rolling green lawn towards the main portico of the palace. Either side of the carpet, huge immobile Guinea-men stood with flaring torches to light the way; candles in coloured glass balls had been hung like fairy fruit on the branches of the trees and glowed red, yellow, blue, white among artificial leaves. Every window of the palace was ablaze with light except for the upper two floors where the servants and slaves were quartered under the eaves, and the higher windows of the great central tower where the Commander's own time apparatus was housed. Don Miguel had a sinking feeling that before the night was out at least one person would have been persuaded to take a royal or noble visitor up that tower and show off the gadgetry, involving the miserable technicians in a day's frantic work tomorrow re-adjusting the delicate settings.

The strains of a band playing the currently fashionable dance-music drifted down from the palace. There was at

present a fad for the chanted melodic lines and intense
drumming of the Mohawks, and as Prince of New Castile, of
course, the Commander could have the finest American
musicians at call.

Distantly visible through the huge windows flanking the
entrance door of the main hall Don Miguel made out the
General Officers of the Society waiting to greet the King who
by now was almost at the threshold. Red Bear, inevitably, was
the most readily identifiable, with his heavy black braids of
hair—and, also inevitably, one of the officers was absent,
Father Ramón would not be here until later.

Surrounded by a gaggle of courtiers, the two royal brothers
and the Princess Imperial followed the King towards the
house. Their faces eloquent of their suspicion that these high-
ranking amateurs might have done the valuable barges some
harm, the Society's watermen were taking over the pot-bellied
craft again to paddle them back to the boat-houses. Most of
the temporary crew had already set off in the wake of the
Princes.

"Move, you two!" Sharper than ever, Don Arturo came
bustling across the wharf waving his wand. "Don't you see the
mooring must be cleared? There on the river is the barge of
the Ambassador of the Confederacy—we dare not keep him
waiting!"

Don Miguel might have answered back this time, now the
Commander was out of earshot, but Don Felipe sensibly
warned him against it by closing fingers hard on his upper
arm. Together they obeyed Don Arturo's instructions, while
the watermen hastily shoved off to make room for the next
arrivals.

"Come on, Miguel!" Don Felipe urged. "We don't want to
get fouled up in the Ambassador's train, do we?"

"No, we don't—I'm already fouled up enough." Don Miguel tore his dull gaze away from the looming, lantern-outlined shape moving with plashing oars down the river towards them, and turned in the direction of the lawn. "Expecting to enjoy yourself this evening, are you, Felipe?"

"Me? I can enjoy myself anywhere. But you look as though the hand of doom's been laid on you."

"If so, I know exactly where," sighed Don Miguel ruefully, rubbing the seat of his breeches.

Don Felipe laughed, linked arms with his friend again, and hurried him up the slope towards the lights of the palace.

TWO

The main hall of the palace, the focus of the grand reception, was gorgeously decorated and remarkably warm—a major advantage, in the opinion of most of the younger Licentiates, not because they appreciated the heat themselves but because the pretty girls who'd been invited could show off in their lightest and filmiest gowns. Already over-warm from rowing in his own uncomfortable formal attire, Don Miguel was not impressed. Moreover, his first glance inside informed him that the throng assembled was milling like a disturbed ants' nest. The chaotic comings and goings stemmed from the fact that guests were arriving from both sides of the house: from the roadway as well as from the wharf facing the river. Consequently every few moments a spearhead of Guinea-men would lead a surge of notables one way or the other across the floor so that they could greet newcomers at the door in accordance with the dictates of protocol.

Paradoxically, the sight of this swirl and bustle raised Don Miguel's spirits a trifle. With such a confusion of people it was conceivable that he might contrive to be overlooked, might slip away to a quiet anteroom and savour his mood of gloom in private with a jug of wine. He made a meaningless response to some comment of Don Felipe's concerning the quality of the women here, his eyes roving around in search of a way to escape.

And then he heard his name called.

His spirits sank again as he turned and saw Red Bear gesturing at him imperiously *en route* from the riverside entrance—where the Ambassador of the Confederacy had just come in—towards the landward door. A summons like that could hardly be ignored. He moved in Red Bear's wake, and Don Felipe, who had also been signalled to, accompanied him.

"I think we're going to enjoy this," Don Felipe said softly. "Do you see who that is who just turned up?"

The major-domo at the land entrance had a fine voice, but the babble of conversation and the noise of the band made it hard to recognise the names he called out. Don Felipe presumably was referring to the group of three—an elderly man and two young girls—who were pausing in the centre of the wide double doorway, but Don Miguel did not recognise any of them.

He was about to say so, when Red Bear, having greeted the trio, turned and again beckoned to them. They strode forward and bowed.

"Your Grace!" One had the feeling that this formality and routine appealed to Red Bear, with his Mohawk background. "I have much pleasure in presenting Don Felipe Basso, Licentiate in Ordinary of the Society of Time, and Don

Miguel Navarro, Licentiate in Ordinary, Companion of the
Order of the Scythe and Hourglass. Don Miguel, Don Felipe:
His Grace the Duke of Scania, Ambassador of the United
Kingdoms of Sweden and Norroway—the Lady Ingeborg, the
Lady Kristina."

His daughters, presumably. Bowing again, Don Miguel
took a second look at them. The were very much alike, and
also very much like the Duke—tall, slender, with the shining
fair hair which on their father's leonine head was turning to
snow-white. Their eyes were large and blue, their complexions
were like milk, and their gowns were clearly designed by a
master. Without ornament or embroidery they managed to
look dazzling and put the baroque finery of most of the other
women to shame.

"Honoured!" Don Felipe said with enthusiasm, and Don
Miguel echoed him as convincingly as he could.

"Don Miguel, Don Felipe," Red Bear concluded, "I charge
you with the duty—which I'm sure you'll find a pleasant
one—of escorting these beautiful young ladies for the
evening."

Don Felipe bowed yet again, this time with a tremendous
flourish, and grinned like a satisfied cat. The Lady Ingeborg's
eyes danced. She was, Don Miguel, judged, by a year or so the
younger of the pair.

By comparison with Don Felipe, he himself felt like a boor
as he uttered some kind of empty acknowledgment. It was
not that the Lady Kristina, opposite whom he happened to
find himself, was not extremely lovely. It was simply that in
his present mood the last kind of company he had been
looking forward to was that of an emancipated girl. He had
never been in Sweden or Norroway, which formed a curious
private enclave where the people followed a schismatic re-

ligion and determinedly minded their own business, refusing
to ally themselves with either the Empire or the Confederacy,
but he did know that under their system women were even
allowed to vote for the members of the Thing, and all his
friends who had trifled with girls from that part of the world
had warned him that they liked—indeed, demanded—to be
treated as at home.

And for the time being at least his recent brush with the
Marquesa had soured him completely on the subject of sexual
equality.

Possibly the daughters of a Duke would be a little more
conventional in their behaviour . . .? No, they wouldn't. No
other girls of such rank would conceivably have arrived at a
reception like this without at least a duenna apiece and
probably half a dozen ladies in attendance.

Oh well . . .

"I'm sure you'll be properly looked after, my dears," the
Duke said in excellent Spanish, smiling at his daughters. "Go
ahead and enjoy yourselves. I've already seen several people I
promised to have a word with tonight, so there's no need for
anyone to look after me." He nodded at Red Bear.

Don Miguel repressed an urge to sigh.

The first steps were automatic: provision of refreshment, a
few comments about how mild the weather had been, and a
reference to the mock battle of the afternoon. And there Don
Miguel's imagination ran dry. For some reason his mind
wandered off down a side-alley dictated by his sore hands and
memory of the hard rower's bench, and when he reverted to
the present he found himself at the tail end of a long and
discourteous silence. Don Felipe and the Lady Ingeborg were
chatting with immense animation on the other side of a large

pillar around which all four of them seemed to have taken station, but he was standing like a booby.

It was a great relief when the Lady Kristina decided to make good his deficiencies for him with that northern directness he had expected to find repellent. She raised a finger to touch the star hanging on the breast of his ruffled shirt.

"Navarro," she said thoughtfully. "Of course. Aren't you the Don Miguel Navarro who was responsible for sorting out that matter of the Aztec mask which could have been such a disaster?" She spoke Spanish as well as her father.

Somewhat uncomfortably, Don Miguel nodded. He said, "As a matter of fact . . . But how on earth did you know? It's not—uh—a matter of public record, exactly."

Lady Kristina gave a quicksilver laugh. "Oh, your hidalgo modesty, Don Miguel! Don't you sometimes carry it too far, here in the Empire? Even if it wasn't spelled out in all the newspapers, something which leads to the award of what you're wearing is bound to become a subject for gossip. And you must know that of all places an embassy is where gossip—particularly scandalous gossip—comes quickest home to roost."

She gave a mischievous chuckle, and Don Miguel felt a responsive smile come lopsided to his own face. He said, "In that case, my lady, I'm sure gossip must have greatly exaggerated the part I played in the affair."

She shrugged the creamy bare shoulders that rose from her plain but exquisite gown. "No doubt, no doubt! But I'm sure that if I were to ask you to tell me what actually happened, you'd underplay your own part grossly and persuade yourself that you were being honest."

Reflexively, stiff defensive words formed on Don Miguel's lips, triggered by the suspicion that she was going to ask him

to give his version, oiling the request with the sort of gushing
flattery he would have expected from someone like—oh,
Catalina di Jorque, for example. He was about to say, "I'm
afraid I can't talk about it. It's confidential to the Society of
Time."

Barely in time he realised she wasn't going to ask him to do
anything of the kind, but was turning to find a place for the
empty glass she held and saying, "Well, if you're not willing to
converse with me, you might ask me to dance."

Somewhat disconcerted, he led her out on the floor. She
was a very good dancer indeed, with an athletic grace far
removed from the usual maidenly shuffle of the partners he
was used to. Though unfamiliar, he found its vigour refreshing, and he was almost enjoying himself by the end of their
first circuit of the hall.

And he wasn't the only one, he noticed, passing Don Felipe
and Lady Ingeborg. Over her beautiful shoulder he saw his
friend give a conspiratorial wink, which the girl could not
have seen because they were already cheek-to-cheek. It looked
as though some of the more slanderous allegations made
about Scandinavian girls might be based on a grain of truth,
even if the girls concerned *were* daughters of a—

His mind made an abrupt jump and he stopped dancing in
mid-beat.

"What on earth—?" Lady Kristina began. She turned and
followed Don Miguel's gaze. "Oh-oh!" she said under her
breath. "Would you like to dodge out of sight?"

He did in fact want to disappear much too much to wonder
why she should suggest it; automatically giving her his arm to
lead her off the floor, he allowed himself to be guided down
one of the nearer side-passages leading away from the hall. It
was not until they were safely around a corner that he

completed his double-take and looked at her, startled.

"Uh—I'm dreadfully sorry!" he exclaimed.

"Why?"

"Well—to snatch you away like that. It was unforgivably rude. You must think I'm an absolute boor."

She gave her quicksilver laugh again, this time throwing back her head and making the most of it. "My dear Don Miguel, let's work this out! Wasn't that the Marquesa di Jorque you just saw arriving?"

He nodded.

"And, gossip or not, isn't it true that you were recently involved in something which made her look like a fool in public?"

He nodded again.

"And weren't you shaken to the core to find her suddenly materialising at a function you didn't think she'd get invited to in a million years?"

He found his voice again. "Yes, my lady," he admitted ruefully. "I can only assume that some friend or relative of hers—ah—wangled her an invitation to make up for the way the Society recently snubbed her."

"So you very naturally want to keep out of her way. Well, I've no objection. What little I know about you suggests that you might be quite an interesting person inside your shell, and what I know about Catalina di Jorque suggests she's worth going out of your way to avoid. Let's find somewhere to sit down and chat, shall we? I presume these rooms are open for us. And, by the way, stop calling me 'my lady'—no one ever calls me that at home except peasants and tradesmen. My name's Kristina." She was opening the nearest door and peeping through it. "Yes, this'll do. And let's have some drinks to keep us going."

Don Miguel, slightly dazed, caught up with her at that point. He glanced around, spotted a Guinea-girl carrying a tray of wine across the next junction of the passage, and called to her. Obediently she followed them into the room and served them with a curtsey.

Kristina took six glasses off the tray and ranged them on a handy table, somewhat to the Guinea-girl's surprise. When the slave moved to go, she gazed after her. As the door closed, she said, "Hmmm! Lovely! I wish I looked like her. Guinea-girls are so sexy, don't you think? Don Miguel, I like you. You shock beautifully. It lights your face from inside like the candles in those glass globes they've hung all over the trees."

She sat down on the end of a heavily-padded sofa with gilt-tooled leather upholstery and helped herself to the nearest glass of wine from the table. Don Miguel hastily copied her so he could respond to her cry of, "Skol!"

Wiping her lip, she went on, "Tell me something, though. It was obvious even before the Marquesa di Jorque turned up that you aren't enjoying yourself. I hope it isn't my fault—though if it is you only have to say so, because I won't be offended. I hate this stuffy business of foisting off people on one another just so as to keep an even count of couples, and I certainly won't object to being abandoned—"

"Not at all, not at all!" Don Miguel broke in. "It's nothing to do with my being asked to escort you."

"In that case, presumably it's the prospect of sweating your way through the rest of the evening which makes you so gloomy. Tell me, what's most likely to happen?"

Don Miguel's defences suddenly crumbled. It was impossible not to be taken with this engagingly frank young woman. He chuckled, and the mirth lifted clouds from his mind.

"To be completely honest," he said, "what will most probably happen is this. Red Bear, who has the Mohawk weakness for firewater, will decide around nine or ten o'clock that he's a better drummer than the professional musicians. He will embarrass *everybody*. The Ambassador of the Confederacy will make slighting remarks about our celebrations, comparing them unfavourably with the winter carnival on the Neva. Everyone will drink furiously because the conversation keeps falling flat in mid-run. Around midnight Father Ramón will arrive to celebrate Mass in the Society's chapel, and we'll be rid of the royals after that. Whereupon we shall be able to get down off our dignity and maybe have some fun with the younger Licentiates and Probationers—those who are here. Most of them aren't. They've had enough sense to stay out in the city and enjoy themselves, except for whichever poor fellow is on duty at the Headquarters Office."

"It sounds daunting," Kristina murmured thoughtfully. "I'd rather be with people who are genuinely enjoying themselves . . . You have to be at this midnight Mass, I suppose?"

Don Miguel nodded vigorously. "Every member of the Society who's sober—and that means you'd damned well better at least *look* sober!—is obliged to attend. It's one of the great events of our year."

He refrained from adding details of what made it such a special occasion. There were certain matters which one simply could not mention to outsiders.

Kristina reached a sudden decision. Rising to her feet, she said with determination, "Miguel, let's go and be with people who are having fun! There's plenty of time to get into Londres and still be back for your services at midnight, isn't there? How about seeing if you can find us a carriage?"

Astonished almost beyond description, Don Miguel felt his

jaw drop. Painfully raising it again, he said, "You know—that's an absolutely wonderful idea!"

THREE

There was no doubt about it, Don Miguel thought contentedly, this was a far, far better way to spend New Year's Eve than at the Commander's palace: wandering among the crowds of merrymakers with a beautiful girl on his arm, doing idiotic things for no particular purpose behind the customary anonymity of half-masks bought from a pedlar, and laughing more and more often than he could remember laughing in his life before. He was naturally a serious person. It occurred to him that perhaps he was habitually too serious.

They had left their carriage shortly after reaching the north side of the river. They had sampled hot chestnuts and hot spiced wine from stalls on wheels, paused to watch a tumbler and juggler for a while, looked in at a display of animals from Africa on Queen Isabela Avenue, joined in the rowdy singing of a troupe of street comedians. Now at last they had come to the hub of the city, to Empire Circle where five wide boulevards met. Here a bonfire was spitting and snarling as people threw fireworks into it; a band was playing traditional tunes, and people danced in the roadway by the light of the flames.

It had turned much colder in the past hour or so, and Kristina, with only a light carriage-cloak covering her flimsy gown, ran forward to warm her hands at the fire. She tossed her long hair back and looked round at him, her eyes sparkling behind her black mask.

"Ah, Miguel! I hadn't thought the people of these damp and misty islands knew so well how to amuse themselves!"

"Oh, we Spanish brought some sunlight from the south when we conquered England, and a trace of it still lingers in our bones," Don Miguel returned with a grin. "It's true you'll find people, here and there, who inveigh against festivities like these as though there were something sinful about having a good time, but thank goodness the mass of the public are too sensible to listen to their arguments. Is what you've seen much different from what you find in your own country?"

"Oh, only on the surface. Of course it's far colder at home, so we go skiing, or sleighing, for months on end while the snow lasts. But the principle's the same." She rubbed her hands together one last time at the fire and turned away, her cheeks reddened by the warmth. "Why, Miguel, you look sad all of a sudden! What's wrong?"

"I was thinking . . ." He hesitated. Normally he would not have spoken of what was in his mind to a girl, whether or not she was of noble birth. However, Kristina was considerably different from any other girl of twenty that he'd met.

"I was thinking," he continued slowly, "of other festivals I've seen, at other places and times. The Aztec feast, for instance, in honour of Xipe the Flayed God, where the

officiating priests were dressed in human skins and there was
ritual cannibalism after the victims had their hearts torn
out."

"You've seen that?"

"Yes, I've seen that. And the *Ludi* in the Circus Maximus
at Rome, where men died for no better reason than to glut the
blood-lust of the crowd . . . And . . ." He ended the remark
with a shrug.

"No wonder you're such a grim person," Kristina said after
a pause. "I'm sorry that I mocked you for it earlier. It must be
a terrible burden to carry in the memory."

"No, not so much as one might think. For one comes back,
you see, to innocent merriment such as this. The prudish and
puritanical who so roundly condemn the gaiety of New Year's
Eve ought to be ashamed of themselves, *I* think. This is
certainly one way in which the world has altered for the better.
How would they feel if we still murdered people publicly, just
to provide a spectacle?"

Kristina gave a sober nod of agreement, and there was a
pause. Then, uttering a quick light laugh, she took his arm
and began to move away from the fire.

"Ah, that chance to warm myself was very welcome.
Strange, when it's far less cold here than at home, how I feel
the chill go clear to my marrow. It must be the dampness, I
suppose, which I'm simply not used to. How do you suppose
she endures it, for example?" She shook a hand free of her
ˆloak and raised it to point across the roadway.

For a moment, Don Miguel did not see what she meant, but
a couple of youths nearby also caught the movement and
glanced up, and one of them whistled in amazement. "Look!"
he urged his companion. "Look there, I say. What do you
make of that?"

His friend's eyes bulged. "Drunk, or mad, to behave like that!" he exclaimed. "Probably mad!"

"An interesting kind of madness," the first youth said.

Don Miguel's reaction, too, at first sight of the subject of their remarks was to assume she must be out of her mind. For one thing her costume—even for a night given over to fancy dress—was ridiculous. It appeared to consist of blue feathers pasted directly on to her skin, on her hips and buttocks and on her belly as high as her navel. There were low red shoes on her feet; around her wrists were beaded bands of various colours, and aside from that she wore only designs in yellow paint on her face, shoulders and breasts. She seemed to have emerged from the southward-leading avenue connecting Empire Circle with the river embankment, and was standing now in the middle of the roadway staring about her. She seemed both dazzled by the sudden brightness here and dazed by her surroundings, for she glanced wildly from side to side like a trapped animal seeking a way of escape.

Ribald yells went up from the crowd and the noise of singing died as people turned to stare. Not far from Kristina and Don Miguel were a pair of civil guards; an indignant man of middle age marched up to them and spoke in furious tone, pointing at the feathered girl. Don Miguel did not catch the actual words, but their import was clear, for a grinning youth next to him bellowed, "Speak for yourself—some of us like to see 'em that way!"

It occurred to Don Miguel that the sight of someone so nearly unclothed was hardly fit for a duke's daughter, but the realisation was both belated and misplaced, for Kristina, her pretty face set in a frown of curiosity, was staring intently at the girl in blue feathers. She said, "Miguel, I've never seen a costume anything like hers before. Where do you suppose it comes from—a tropical country? Asia, Africa . . .?"

Something clicked in Don Miguel's mind. The word
"premonition" flicked through his thoughts. But he did not
try to pin the idea down. A group of drunken workmen at the
edge of the crowd nearest to where the feathered girl was
standing had clearly made up their minds that if she came out
in public half-naked she could expect what they intended to
do to her. Leering, they moved closer to her, about five or six
in a group. Tiger-wise, she paused in her frightened staring
and half-crouched to confront them.

It looked as though the situation was going to turn nasty.

"Kristina," he said in a low voice, "I think I ought to get
you away from here."

"You'd do much better," came the reply as tart as lemon-
juice, "to make these civil guards go and help the poor girl
before those men start to gang-rape her!"

Accustomed to more conventional language from well-bred
young women, Don Miguel was taken aback and so distracted
he failed to witness the next development. A sudden cry drew
his attention back to the feathered girl, and he saw in
amazement that one of the workmen was lying prostrate on
the hard ground and she was in the process of hurling another
of her assailants over her shoulder in a perfect wrestling
throw.

"Oh, lovely!" Kristina clapped her hands, then caught Don
Miguel by the arm. "Come on, let's go and cheer her!"

But the ferment of her earlier remark was working in his
mind by now, and the premonition was coming clearer.

Never seen a costume anything like hers before . . .

What was he doing standing here like a petrified dummy?
He started to shoulder his way towards the feathered girl as
violently and rapidly as he dared, ignoring the complaints of

those other bystanders he had to push aside. Somehow Kristina kept up with him.

By the time he made it to the clear patch of ground surrounding the girl, two more men had joined the first on the pavement, bruised and cursing, and the girl was spitting what were obviously insults at them. Her voice was almost as deep and strong as a man's despite the fact that she was shorter than Kristina. Listening, Don Miguel felt the hairs on his nape start to prickle.

The girl was small and thin, but wiry. Now he was close enough he could see that she had black hair dressed in stiff wings either side of her head. Her complexion was olive-sallow. And the words she was uttering sounded like— *like*, not the same as—the language of Cathay.

Don Miguel was as well acquainted with the costumes, customs and languages of the major civilisations of history as any Licentiate of similar experience, and better than most. He could make himself understood in Attic Greek and Quechua, Phoenician and Latin, Persian and Aramaic. He could also recognise the characteristic vowel-consonant clusters of many other tongues which he did not speak fluently. And what the girl was hissing at her attackers did not fit any language he could call to mind.

The most obvious and most logical explanation for her presence was that she must be a legitimate visitor to Londres —perhaps a member of the Cathayan ambassador's train. Under the influence of a brainstorm, or having taken some foreign drug or potent liquor, she might have lost her senses and run off ...

But in that case you'd expect her to be a mere dancing-girl or geisha. You wouldn't expect her to be capable of throwing burly workmen aside as though they were straw-filled dummies.

It simply didn't figure!

In his worried concentration, he had taken another couple of paces in the girl's direction, and the second was one too many. Suddenly, without warning, she screamed and hurled herself at him.

He reacted barely in time. She was not merely a wrestler, he discovered to his dismay. She was a killing fighter, fantastic though that was in view of her sex. Her first move had been to launch a crippling kick at his crotch, and the best he could manage was to twist aside so that her toe struck his thigh instead. Even so, the force of the kick caused him to lose his footing. He had to go down on one knee, fending her off from below, and she seized his right arm at wrist and elbow and gave it such a violent wrench he thought she might dislocate the joint. Pivoting frantically on his pinioned arm and knee, he swept his other leg through a half-circle and knocked her feet from under her. She was unbelievably strong for her build, but she was light, and that was something she could do nothing about.

Losing her grip on his arm, she tumbled sideways, rolled free, and came back at him with a lightning-fast leap, head aimed for a butt in his belly. In his turn he rolled, hoping with a distant corner of his mind that street-dirt was not going to foul his cloak and breeches too badly for him to return to the palace, and with joined legs flung her slamming over his head to measure her length behind him. Recovering faster than he could, she wheeled around and tried to sink her teeth into his thigh as he scrambled to prevent her rising again. Clumsily he fell on her, and pinned her wrists and one leg to the ground in an improvised but serviceable hold which exploited his superior weight. Then, by main force, he started to bring her wrists together.

She said nothing, but set her jaw grimly and stared up at him, straining to dislodge his grip. During that long moment Don Miguel found time to hope prayerfully that there were no Licentiates or Probationers in the crowd around who might recognise him behind his half-mask. If there was anything more undignified that a member of the Society could do than wrestle with a woman in the middle of Empire Circle, he couldn't imagine it.

All right, there was no alternative, however much it went against his principles. Woman or no, he was going to have to hurt her. He shifted his fingers on her wrists and stabbed down at the ganglia.

The shock went all the way through her. She forgot about resistance for long enough to let him seize both wrists in one hand and cramp them together, still applying the agonising pressure. With the hand thus released he sought the carotid arteries in her neck and scientifically began to strangle her.

In fifteen seconds she was limp. He gave her a little longer to ensure that she would not recover too quickly, and then sat wearily on his heels, wiping sweat from his forehead. Mingled now with the encouraging cries of the crowd, of which he had barely been aware during the struggle, he now heard voices of complaint directed at his "ruthless" treatment of the feathered girl.

Ruthless! *Those people should have had to tackle her*!

But the situation must be regulated straight away. Where the blazes were those civil guards he'd seen standing near the bonfire? As the saying went, the only time you couldn't find a guard was when you wanted one—

Ah, here they were, officiously thrusting their way among the crowd to the accompaniment of good-humoured mockery.

He got to his feet.

"Make these people stand back!" he ordered crisply. "Get a hackney-carriage and help me load this girl into it!"

The civil guards bridled. One of them, bristling his mustachios, demanded, "Who do you think *you* are, then?" He dropped his hand to his sword-hilt.

Don Miguel drew a deep breath. "Do as I say! I'm Don Miguel Navarro of the Society of Time, and this is Society business. Jump to it, you fools!"

The scar across his face made him look savage and very much a man to be obeyed, but it was the talisman-like name of the Society which caused the guards to blanch and comply, and imposed a startled hush on the crowd followed by a ripple of comment.

Taking off his cloak, Don Miguel laid it over the girl on the ground. She was stirring a little already, though still a long way from regaining consciousness. It would be advisable to tie her hands and ankles, he decided. The kerchief he had in his pocket would serve for the former. When he looked around for something longer to go round her legs, something dangled before his eyes. Glancing up, he saw that Kristina had eluded the civil guards and was offering him the girdle of her gown. He took it with a word of thanks and knotted it fast.

"Who is she?" Kristina demanded. "Why did she attack you when you hadn't threatened her?"

"I don't know who she is," Don Miguel grunted. "But if she's what I think she might be, there's going to be the devil to pay tonight."

FOUR

In the dark padded interior of the hackney-carriage they sat mostly in silence, staring at the cloak-shrouded form of the girl laid along the opposite seat as successive scythe-sweeps of light from roadside lanterns moved over her.

Suddenly Kristina shivered and pressed up against Don Miguel. She said, "Miguel, what did you mean when you said there'd be the devil to pay tonight? You sounded so fierce, I was frightened."

Already Don Miguel regretted that he had spoken. More than that, he regretted having acted with so little to go on —yet what alternative had there been? If his vague, ill-formulated, horrifying suspicions were correct, and the girl had been taken into custody by the ordinary civil guards and some unimaginative local justice of the peace had stumbled on her origins . . .

Potentially it would be like opening a second Pandora's

Box, and perhaps this time there might not even be hope left at the bottom.

Of course, far more likely was that the mystery would be satisfactorily explained in everyday terms tomorrow morning, and he'd earn himself a severe reprimand from the General Officers. Right now, he hardly dared guess at the outcome.

He said apologetically, "If you don't mind, Kristina, I'd rather not tell you any more until I've had a chance to investigate."

She glanced at him, lips a little parted as though about to ask another question, but decided not to and merely clung closer than ever at his side. He stroked her arm comfortingly and wished that the driver would hurry.

This feathered girl frightened him! Kristina had been right about her costume—it was nothing remotely like any that he'd seen pictured from anywhere in the modern world. Worse still, it was like nothing he'd chanced across in his study of history. And as to the language she'd spoken . . .

He choked the thought off with an effort as the carriage wheeled with a grating of iron tyres on cobbles and drew up in the forecourt of the Society's Headquarters Office.

Like the Commander's palace, it was set in large and handsome grounds; like the palace, too, it was dominated by a tall tower housing time apparatus. There the resemblance ended. It was completely in darkness tonight, but for a single yellow square of a window on the ground floor near the main door and two flambeaux in sconces under the porch.

Jumping from the step of the carriage almost before it had halted, Don Miguel uttered an oath under his breath. Tonight, naturally, there might be only the duty Probationer in the entire building—but also, just possibly, the man he needed to see more desperately than anyone in the world.

"Get the girl out!" he rapped to the driver. "I'll have the door opened."

The man nodded and clambered down from his high seat, while the horses shifted uneasily in the traces. Don Miguel started up the dark steps.

The door opened before he reached it, and there stood a young man blinking diffidently in the light of the flambeaux. He was twenty or less, snub-nosed, blue-eyed, below Don Miguel in height but well enough built.

"Are you alone?" Don Miguel flung at him.

..."Ah—yes, Licentiate!" the young man said. "I'm Probationer Jones, sir, on duty tonight of course. I believe your honour is Don Miguel Navarro. What service can I do you?"

"You're *completely* alone? No one else is here at all?"

"*Absolutely* no one, sir," Jones declared, eyes wide with surprise at the force of the question.

Don Miguel's heart sank. So the agony of apprehension must drag on longer yet. Still, there was no help for that. He passed a weary hand across his forehead.

"There's a girl in my carriage," he said. "She ought not to be here, or anywhere else, for that matter. I'm having her brought inside."

Jones gave a sigh. "Very well, sir. I presume you'll want a suite in the quarters upstairs, and privacy—"

The look on Don Miguel's face made him break off, stuttering with confusion.

"Have members of the Society required such services of you?" Don Miguel demanded.

"Uh . . ." Jones's embarrassment was acute. "Not me personally, sir. But I believe other probationers. Uh . . ."

"If anyone ever tries it on you, report him to your Chief Instructor. It's no part of your duties to act as a pander.

Understood?" Without waiting for an answer Don Miguel swung around and discovered that Jones's mistake was a very natural one, for Kristina was clearly in view standing by the door of the carriage, while the driver was still half-hidden in shadow as he wrestled to lift the cloak-enveloped form of the feathered girl.

"Help the driver with his burden," he snapped at Jones. "Show him to a room inside where there's a couch or something he can put her on."

"At once, sir," Jones said, and hurried down the steps with his cheeks as red as fire.

"Kristina," Don Miguel said in a low voice, moving close to her, "I'm sorry to have had to drag you here. But it looks as though I can't find anyone to help me unless I go back to the palace. So at least I can return you to your father now."

"You have to go back soon anyway, don't you?" she countered. "It's gone eleven—nearly a quarter past!"

"Is it?" Don Miguel exclaimed in dismay. "Then I'm an idiot! I came here on a fool's errand. You see, I must have some advice from Father Ramón, and thought he might still be in his office here—but of course, if it's so late, he'll already be on his way to the Commander's palace. My wits must be woolgathering. Lord! Lord! What a mess!"

He pulled himself together with an effort. "Get back in the carriage, then. I have one more thing to attend to before we leave."

He spun on his heel and dashed indoors.

When he came back, instead of rejoining Kristina inside the carriage, he scrambled up to the driver's box and seized the reins. The horses whinnied and leaned on the traces, and Kristina cried out in surprise.

"Sorry!" Don Miguel shouted down to her over the grind and clatter of the wheels. "But that feathered girl is far too dangerous to leave in the charge of one young man like Jones! So I paid the driver to stay and help stand guard. Don't worry—I'm not a bad driver, though I say so myself!"

The forced jocularity of his tone concealed an ever-growing sense of alarm. He had told Kristina only one of the reasons why he had needed to go into the building. In addition, he had hastened up the tower in which the time-halls were located, and made sure that the great locks on their doors had not been tampered with. And they had not. Jones was indeed alone as he had claimed.

There had been the slim possibility that some drunken Probationers, or even corrupt Licentiates, might have taken the chance offered by the absence of everyone except Jones to secure unlawful access to the time apparatus. The consequences of that kind of prank would have been bad enough, but rectifiable.

Now it seemed virtually certain that something far worse must have happened.

A cold wind was blowing along the river now; their route followed the embankment. He shivered and damned the impatience which had prevented him from reclaiming the cloak he'd used to wrap around the feathered girl.

Driving like a fury, he brought the carriage swiftly to broad, straight Holy Cross Avenue—the last portion of their route on the north side of the river. At the next bridge they would have to swing right and cross over. And there, at the approach to the bridge, there was some sort of commotion. At first he took it for the expected crowd of people coming across from the south to attend Mass at midnight in the cathedrals of the city; it was not until the carriage was already engulfed in a wave of

pale-faced, terrified men, women and children that he heard
the near-screams of civil guards trying to keep order and
realised that this was nothing so commonplace. The whole
roadway was flooded with fugitives in the grip of panic; the
windows of nearby houses were being flung up as the
occupants heard the racket outside, and the air was full of a
confused moaning.

Kristina leaned from the carriage window as he slowed
perforce to a crawl. "Miguel, what's happening?" she cried.

"I don't know!" he answered curtly. "Guard! Guard!"

A civil guard on horseback, breasting the crowd as though
fording a river in spate, forged slowly in their direction,
waving a gauntleted hand. When he came close enough, he
called out, "You'll have to go around another way, your
honour! It's impossible to get past here!"

Don Miguel stared, cursing the murky darkness which the
lanterns barely relieved. Under the bridge, too, there was a
disturbance; he heard the loud splashing of water.

"What's going on?" he bawled.

"No one seems to be sure, your honour! Some say it's an
invasion, some say rioting—but either way, across the river
there it's total chaos!" The guard sounded frightened. "Men's
bodies have been seen floating downstream, stuck full of
arrows, they say! And there are fires!"

Shriller and more piercing than the general tumult, there
was suddenly a scream from near the bridge, and people
began incontinently trying to run. Ignoring the guard and
Don Miguel, they surged past the carriage, making it rock.

The guard wheeled his horse and went off shouting, trying
to restore some calm to the crowd with reassuring lies. There
was no hope of forcing the carriage nearer to the bridge now,
short of running down the people who were in its way, and the

best Don Miguel could manage was by jerking the reins to
sidle the horses on to the verge of the road. Even to cover
those few paces took a heartbreakingly long time. He set the
brake and leapt down from the box.

Kristina was still peering pale-faced from the window. As
she saw him descend, she threw open the door and made to
step down also. He gestured her to stay where she was.

"I'll see if I can get one of the civil guards to escort you
away," he promised. "This is no place for—"

"Miguel, if you throw my sex at me one more time I'll lose
my temper! I'm coming with you. The guards have all the
work they can cope with, and I'm not going to be left sitting in
the carriage here when there may be something useful I can
do!"

Defiantly she jumped to the ground and belted the sash of
her cloak around her in a businesslike manner. Displeased,
but realising the futility of argument with this strong-willed
young woman, Don Miguel took her arm and together they
forced a way to the broad half-moon of pavement on to which
traffic from the bridge debouched.

Here the confusion was fantastic. A small detachment of
soldiers with horse-borne light artillery had formed up at the
parapet of the bridge as though expecting an assault at any
moment, but their officer seemed to have realised that that
was a false alarm and was detailing them now to help with
crowd-control instead, occasionally pausing to look up- and
down-river with a spyglass. On the south bank blurs of red
could be seen, indistinct because of traces of mist rising from
the water; these must be the fires the guard had told Don
Miguel about. He wondered how many of the fugitives had
lost the homes they had abandoned half-clad, and to what
disaster . . .

Having redeployed his men, the officer in charge of the artillery troop—a handsomely uniformed young man on a fine roan gelding—began to move in their direction, and Don Miguel attracted his attention by shouting and waving.

"Miguel Navarro, Society of Time!" he introduced himself, cupping his hands to his mouth. "What's the chance of getting over the river to the palace?"

The officer stared down at him as though he were mad. He said explosively, "To the palace? You're lucky to be here, aren't you, rather than there?"

Don Miguel felt as though an icy hand had been laid on his bare brain. He said, "I'm afraid I've no clear idea of what's going on!"

"No more have I—" The officer's horse started at some alarm, and danced sideways three half-paces before willing to be quieted. "But whatever devilry it is, it's far worse there than here! Haven't you looked across the river? Here, take my glass!"

He handed the instrument to Don Miguel, who set it to his eye and turned to the south. Instantly, what had been mere reddish blurs, half-masked by mist, formed a coherent pattern with what few landmarks could be seen. He burst out, "It's the palace that's on fire!"

"Correct!" The officer laughed without humour, reclaiming the spyglass. "One of my men reported a minute ago that the roof is falling in."

"But the King's there, and the Prince Imperial, and the Commander of the Society, and the Ambassador of the Confederacy—!"

The hand on his arm tightened. He glanced down at Kristina and saw that the colour had drained from her face. Yes: her father and her sister, too . . .

"God knows what it's all about!" the officer said savagely.
"But it's the biggest disaster in a hundred years, no question
of that. The night on the other side of the river is alive with
murderous shadows, killing and looting and burning."

From near the water's edge, down-slope from the embankment, came a loud exclamation. "Someone out there—swimming! Someone help him! Someone get him ashore!"

"Sounds like a job I can tackle," the officer snapped, and
dug his heels into his horse's flanks, departing with a
sketched salute to Kristina. He called together three or four of
his soldiers, who ran down with ropes to help the swimmer.
Don Miguel and Kristina followed them. If by a miracle this
was a man who had managed to get across from the south
bank, he might have more exact news.

They arrived as the man was being hauled out. He had
spent his last strength, and could not stand; he collapsed face
downwards on the ground. Don Miguel saw with horror that
each of his shoulders was stuck with a short, vicious arrow,
the barbs buried deep in the flesh. It was a miracle he had
kept afloat.

"Miguel!" Kristina whispered. "Isn't it your friend?"

Don Miguel strode forward. "God's name," he said.
"God's name, but it is. Felipe!"

He dropped on one knee beside the stricken form, but the
officer, dismounting, waved him back. "Wait!" he snapped.
"Wait till they've drained the water from his lungs!"

With a muttered apology Don Miguel drew aside, and a
medical orderly from the artillery troop hurried up with a case
of medicines. Like a huge waddling white owl a Sister of
Mercy came after him.

Aching, Don Miguel watched as they inspected the arrows
and prepared to extract them and dress the wounds. He

ignored the continuing noise from all around and was only dimly aware that the flow of refugees across the bridge had dropped to a final trickle of the sick, the aged and the very young.

Abruptly his preoccupation was shattered by the rattle of a carriage from behind him, on the approach to the bridge. A harsh voice called out to its driver, telling him to go around another way.

Then another voice was heard, speaking from the interior of the carriage, dry and precise. "But I must cross here and now to go to the Prince's palace. I must be there before midnight."

Don Miguel's relief was so great he almost swooned. He started forward, waving and shouting at the top of his lungs.

"Father Ramón! Father Ramón! Praise heaven you're here!"

FIVE

The Jesuit master-theoretician of the Society of Time stepped down from his carriage, brows drawn together on his bird-like face as—for what appeared to be the first time—he surveyed the fantastic scene. The roadway looked like a just-abandoned battlefield, what with the sickly and lame refugees still hobbling past and the scattered belongings which earlier passers-by had found too heavy to carry any further.

He said, "I fail to see, my son, why my arrival in the midst of this to-do should so excite you, but something tells me I ought to find out, even though I don't expect to enjoy learning the answer. Enlighten me."

Rapidly Don Miguel summed up the situation as best he could: the mysterious attackers beyond the river, the setting on fire of the palace, the unknown fate of the royal family, the refugees streaming north, his being in the company of the

Lady Kristina of Scania, her concern about her father . . .

Father Ramón's expression grew more and more horrified.

"I had no idea!" he exclaimed. "It's my practice to pray privately on the way to celebrate Mass, with the curtains of my carriage drawn. I did hear shouting and commotion, but I assumed that fights had broken out among the New Year revellers! Have you any idea what may be at the bottom of it all?"

"I'm very much afraid that I may," Don Miguel said soberly, and described his encounter with the feathered girl in the middle of Empire Circle.

He was appalled to see the expression on the Jesuit's face change still further, beyond mere horror to outright and unconcealed fear.

"Do you know who this woman is?" he demanded.

"Judging by your description, I think I do," Father Ramón answered heavily. "A costume not recognisably of the modern world, nor of any recorded period of history, a language you could not identify . . . But that is the worst possible conclusion we could jump to, unless we are goaded beyond any alternative. Is there any way we can get recent news of events the other side of the river?"

"Ah—yes, with luck there may be!" Don Miguel said. "Just before you arrived, Don Felipe Basso swam the river pierced with strange arrows. See, they're ministering to him on the river-bank." He pointed.

Father Ramón headed towards the white silhouette of the Sister of Mercy like a shot from a gun. Don Miguel glanced at Kristina; it was clear from her paleness and her trembling lips that her self-control was stretched nearly to the limit. He put his arm around her reassuringly and led her in the wake of Father Ramón.

The Jesuit was already kneeling at Don Felipe's side when they caught up. Turning his head to the medical orderly, he snapped, "Will he live?" If the answer was negative, of course, Extreme Unction must precede any questioning. But the medical orderly, tossing bloody dressings into the river, gave a nod.

"He's tough as oak, Father," he said. "He'll live."

Don Miguel heaved a sigh of relief and bent close to listen to what Father Ramón might say. Before the latter could speak, however, Don Felipe had opened his eyes and recognised him.

"Ah, you were lucky, were you, Father?" he whispered. "And . . . You too, Miguel? Heavens, I thought you were . . . No matter, though. That's not the important thing. God's wounds, what can have taken possession of them all?"

"Speak!" commanded Father Ramón sternly. "Without fear or favour I charge you to speak unvarnished truth in the name of the Society!"

Don Felipe closed his eyes again. Lips writhing, in halting whispers he outlined the dreadful tale.

Partly, it seemed the trouble had been the fault of the Ambassador from the Confederacy, notoriously a sneering fellow and a dogmatic chauvinist. As Don Miguel had sardonically prophesied, he had scathingly dismissed the quality of New Year festivity in Londres as grossly inferior to what he could enjoy at home.

Partly it had been the Prince Imperial's fault. It was no secret that now, in his forty-first year, he was growing tired of waiting to succeed his long-lived father, and inclined to dispel his boredom in unprincely pastimes.

And partly, said Don Felipe, it was the fault of Red Bear, whose weakness for firewater was equally well known.

At some time in the evening there had been an exchange of
sharp words. A royal temper flared; there was a reference to
deporting the Ambassador tied face-to-tail on a donkey.
Hovering around the fringes of the royal party, as ever eager
for a smidgin of reflected glory, were two dangerous would-be
conciliators: Don Arturo Cortés, and the Marquesa di Jorque.

"Someone in authority should have smoothed things over,"
Don Felipe moaned. "Red Bear, or even the Commander! But
that damned woman from Jorque hasn't any notion of tact!
She brought up the subject of women's emancipation, and I
think someone must have said men and women could never be
equal, because there are some things like warfare which are
entirely male—and the Ambassador jumped on this as
another chance to disagree on principle, and said the
bloodiest and fiercest fighters in history were the Scythian
Amazons, so the King said the Amazons were a myth, and
appealed to Don Arturo, and . . ."

Breaking off, he coughed violently, and pain from the
arrow-wounds in his back convulsed him in agony. Waiting
for him to recover, Father Ramón knelt at his side more rigid
than a statue.

"And then, my son . . .?" he prompted finally.

"I don't know," whispered Don Felipe. "All I remember
after that is the terrible women with their bows and spears,
swarming down the stairway leading from the central tower. I
stood and fought with those who could fight, but they came on
like devils, and in the end they shattered us to bits."

His voice tailed away.

"My father!" Kristina said in a high thin tone. "My sister!
What became of them?"

But there was no answer. The medical orderly dropped to
feel Don Felipe's pulse. After a moment he turned to Father

Ramón. "We must take him away and let him rest," he said. "Talking has greatly weakened him."

Stiffly Father Ramón rose to his feet. Don Miguel drew him aside and whispered to him urgently.

"I'm still in the dark about all this. *Do* you know who these 'terrible women' are?"

"Almost beyond doubt," the Jesuit said in a dead voice. "Amazons . . . Yes, it hangs together. This is the way it must have happened. They wanted—the fools! The *fools!* God forgive me for condemning them so, but what other name can one use? Listen: they wanted to decide this question about women being valiant fighters, and they sought the answer where they should not have trespassed, beyond the bounds of our reality. Women such as the one you described to me are female gladiators from the court of King Mahendra the White Elephant, in a world where a decadent Indian usurper sits the throne of a Mongol empire governing all Asia and all Europe—a world further distant from our own than any other which our researchers have explored."

Thanks to having been made privy to the best-kept secret of the Society, the explanation made sense to Don Miguel. But he wished it could have been as meaningless to him as it was to Kristina, who had no inkling of the perilous tampering with reality which the Society had embarked on forty years before. She merely repeated as she looked from one to other of her companions, "My father and sister—what became of them?"

He could only give her a meant-to-be comforting squeeze with the arm he had kept around her shoulders.

"Yes—yes, of course, I ought to have realised that . . . But I shouldn't be talking about abstracts; the thing's been done. By whom? Who could have broached this secret to the company—surely not the Commander, even on his father's orders?"

"No, not the Commander. For all that he possesses a degree
of royal arrogance, he would not imagine he could flout
natural law."

"Then—who?"

"The leader of the expedition to that distant stream of
history," said Father Ramón, "was Don Arturo Cortés." On
the last word his mouth shut like a steel trap. There was
silence between them, but the noise of the fugitives continued,
and now, as bells pealed out to announce the imminence of
midnight, they heard also the dry crackle of gunfire.

The orderly and two soldiers were raising Don Felipe from
the ground to set him on a wheeled invalid trolley. The
movement disturbed him, and he gave a sudden cry.

"Father Ramón! Where are you?"

"Here, my son!" The Jesuit darted towards him.

"Father, I did not tell you the worst!" Don Felipe babbled.
"I saw them kill the King! I saw them shoot the Prince
Imperial full of arrows, and they speared men and women
alike as they tried to flee! I saw a girl flung from the head of
the stairway to break her head open on the marble floor! I
saw—God's pity, Father, I saw such monstrous things!"

"What?" said one of the soldiers helping to lift him. And,
before Father Ramón could stop him, he had spun round to
shout to his officer. "Sir! He says the King is dead!"

A hush fell for an instant over all those within earshot of the
cry, and was followed by a sound like a rising gale: "The King
is dead! The King! The King!" The words spread swiftly,
dying away across the sea of people like an echo.

"Father Ramón, is there anything we can do?" demanded
Don Miguel.

For a long moment, his bird-like head bowed, Father

Ramón did not answer. At last however he stirred, and seemed to brisken. He said, "Well, there are some immediate steps, are there not? For example, you might find a civil guard and have criers sent to call in members of the Society who were not attending the palace reception, bidding them come at once to the Headquarters Office. This should be simple— they'll mostly be passing this way to attend our Mass. Then . . Have you a carriage?"

"I had." Don Miguel stared in the direction of the spot where it had been left. "No, it's gone—probably comman- deered by the refugees. Anyway, it would be hard to force a carriage through this fear-crazed crowd."

"So we'll take the horses from mine." Father Ramón shrugged. "It's many years since my aged bones spanned a horse's back, but needs must. To it, and quickly!"

SIX

Never before had Don Miguel tried to ride at speed
bareback, controlling his horse with carriage-reins and at the
same time trying to comfort a weeping girl seated behind him
with her head buried on his shoulder. It was half nightmare,
half farce, and about the only thing which could have made it
worse would have been if Kristina had followed the Empire
custom of riding side-saddle instead of astride like a man. She
would certainly have fallen off if she had.

In spite of his lack of practice on horseback, Father Ramón
made good speed, and Don Miguel had difficulty in making
his own mount keep up, carrying double as it was. However,
by digging his heels in vigorously, he forced the poor beast to
follow close behind, and they galloped up the driveway to the
Headquarters Office neck and neck. By now two or three
more of the windows were lighted, and the front door stood
ajar. At the sound of hoofs on gravel someone came running

to the entrance. It was Jones, and in the light of the porch flambeaux it could be seen that one of his eyes was newly blacked.

"She got loose?" Don Miguel cried in alarm, sliding to the ground and reaching to help Kristina dismount.

"Yes, sir," Jones agreed unhappily. "And we had a terrible job tying her up again."

"But you managed it?"

"With the help of the man you left here, yes, sir. I'd never have coped with her on my own."

And the poor fellow has lost his carriage for his pains, Don Miguel reflected briefly. Still, there were people in Londres tonight who had lost not only their livelihood but their lives. Time enough to consider such problems later. For the present, there was a grand catastrophe to attend to.

"Did you say the girl got loose?" called Father Ramón, awkwardly scrambling from his own horse's back.

"Yes, but was recaptured," Don Miguel answered. "Jones, take us to her quickly!"

Kristina nearly stumbled as she ascended the steps to the entrance. He settled her comfortably in an armchair in the hallway, and saw as he was doing so that instead of turning through the open door of the anteroom in which the driver was grimly standing guard with a club over the feathered girl—tied now with good strong rope, he noticed—Father Ramón was heading into the interior of the building.

"Father! The girl's down here!" he called.

"I know—but come with me, and be quick!"

"Look after the lady," Don Miguel instructed Jones, and dashed in Father Ramón's wake.

The Jesuit led him up the broad main stairway, along the adjacent gallery, past the entrance to the main reference library with its thousands and thousands of books on conventional recorded history as amplified by the researches of the Society's visitors to the past, and halted before the door of a smaller room which Don Miguel had never entered. It was kept firmly locked, and one did not have to ask to realise why. Here were the files, documents and records which the Society's General Officers in their collective wisdom deemed the world not yet ready to understand.

"Have you ever been into the restricted room?" asked Father Ramón, fumbling under his habit for a ring of keys.

"No, never."

"But you know what it contains?"

"Well—well, one presumes data on the most sensitive periods of the past. Perhaps concerning the ministry of Our Lord . . ." Don Miguel made a vague gesture.

"If that were all, we should not need to take such precautions to protect what's kept here," Father Ramón sighed, thrusting home the key and turning it with a click. "In spite of the strictures of so-called 'progressives' and 'rationalists,' Christ was in every aspect so remarkable as to command our eternal admiration. If he had not been, the Church would have crumbled at the first contact we made with the era he inhabited. But one knows that, from the fact that the Church has survived."

As he spoke, he was leading Don Miguel forward among a maze of high dark metal book-stacks, with enormously thick glass doors securely locked to enclose bound volumes, loose files, stacks of periodicals marked down the spine with warning red letters indicating the degree of the contents' secrecy.

"No," the Jesuit continued, "there are things here which comprise a far heavier burden of knowledge than simply proof that Christ was man, and ate and slept and had to relieve himself! But for the inflexible rule that no single person— not even the Commander—may consult these files without a witness beside him, I'd never have compelled you to accompany me. You've been burdened enough already for so young a man. But"—and he halted before one of the padlocked stacks, producing another smaller key—"here is where I must confirm my guess."

Drawing back the glass doors, he reached into the case and selected a fat, bright red volume of manuscript notes. Interleaved with the close-written pages were accurate water-colour drawings. As rapidly as though he were merely looking for something he had already seen—and presumably he was—he turned to one such picture and held it for Don Miguel to examine.

"Does not the woman downstairs resemble that?" he demanded.

Don Miguel nodded slowly. The feathers pasted on the body of the girl here depicted were green, not blue, and the painted designs on her face and torso were white instead of yellow, but the style of the hair was the same, the complexion, the shoes, the beaded ornaments around her wrists.

"Then my worst fears are fulfilled," Father Ramón muttered. He shut the book and thrust it back on the shelf. "And I must confess to you, my son, that I am totally at a loss. This disaster is so completely without precedent that it has scarcely even been speculated upon by our theorists."

To hear Father Ramón, himself the expert of experts in this field, say such a thing shook Don Miguel to the core. Mind numb, he could find no answer worth the uttering.

"Still, there are certain texts here which may suggest a clue, and there are calculations we shall have to perform . . ." The

Jesuit turned to another of the locked cases, and began to run his eye along its contents. "Yes, we may at least expect some guidance from a few of the articles in here. Hold out your arms, Don Miguel; I'm about to impose a physical burden on you as well."

A few minutes later, he cautiously followed Father Ramón down the stairs again, both arms full of heavy books and bound manuscripts. There was confusion in the entrance hall; Jones, who had as yet no clear conception of what was going on, was trying to calm a number of angry Licentiates who had answered the criers' call and returned from their New Year celebrations to the Headquarters Office.

On seeing Father Ramón's grave expression, they fell silent and turned to face him. He paused five or six steps from the bottom of the staircase, where he could overlook them; Don Miguel gratefully seized the chance to rest his load on the banister.

"Father, why were we told to come here?" one of the bolder of the Licentiates called out. "There's a riot or something in the city—wouldn't we be better employed helping to put it down?"

"This isn't a problem to be solved with swords and fists," Father Ramón snapped back. "Before I tell you what it is, though, you tell me something: how goes it out there at the moment?"

"Why, there's chaos! Hordes of people came panicking into the middle of the town, bearing some crazy tale about an attempt to murder the King!"

"But he's dead, definitely," called someone else from the far side of the hallway, and at once there was a clamour of competing voices. Father Ramón stilled it with an imperious gesture, and made them speak one by one. Listening to the picture that emerged by fragments, Don Miguel was chilled all over again, and saw that Kristina, still waiting in the chair where he had left her, had passed the boundary of her endurance and was weeping silently.

Much of what was said he already knew: the palace burning, the river fouled with the flotsam of dead bodies. But other news was fresh, and equally terrifying: a maddened crowd of fugitives on Queen Isabela Avenue had rent a civil guard to pieces, a gang of thieves and looters had snatched the chance to raid the great merchants' stores and were setting fires of their own to distract their pursuers, two army detachments had accidentally begun to fire on each other, imagined their colleagues to be the anticipated enemy, and killed many men before their officers brought them under control . . .

"Enough!" Father Ramón barked at last. "Come with me into the instruction hall and I will make everything clear. Don Miguel! Go through those books I've given you and mark for me every reference you can find which may assist us. I'll rejoin you when I've allotted tasks to occupy our brothers."

The material Don Miguel had to sift through was itself as frightening—after a different fashion—as what he had just heard about the situation in Londres tonight. He had never dreamed of its existence. Turning the pages of book after book, he felt himself hurled headlong into an alien universe even though the names subscribed to the various articles and letters he was reading had been familiar to him since he joined the Society and included all the General Officers, plus such outstanding Licentiates as Don Arturo Cortés and Father Terence O'Dubhlainn.

But the subject they were discussing . . . ! They dizzied him;

one melted into another, and advanced mathematical formulae danced before his eyes. "The Most Probable Implications of a Short-Range Causative Loop"—"Results of a Tentative Experiment in Quasi-Present-Time Spatial Displacement"—"An Exception to the Ground Conditions of the Standard Equation Defining Historical Alterations"—"Reverberative Factors Affecting Recorded Reality in Consequence of an Ink-blot on a Mediaeval Manuscript" . . .

He was almost surprised to discover that there really was a Father Ramón in this world he inhabited, that he had returned from his briefing of the other members of the Society who had answered the emergency call, and that he was standing by the table and waiting for a verdict on the task he had set.

"Well? What have you found most useful out of this lot?"

"Practically nothing, Father," Don Miguel sighed. "The whole subject is so strange to me! I think I follow most of the reasoning—my mathematical knowledge is strained, but the symbols and the operators are clearly enough defined—but when it comes to arguing out the implications . . . Well, for better or worse, these are the items I've picked out for you."

He laid four of the books in the centre of the table, each marked with a scrap of paper to locate the most promising articles they contained, and vacated his chair to let Father Ramón sit down. Impatiently he waited while the Jesuit raced through the texts.

"I see what you mean," he admitted at length. "It's a matter of scale, naturally. It's one thing to analyse the effect of an accidental ink-blot which one suspects of having been caused through the inadvertence of a time-traveller; it's another question altogether when it comes to people being killed."

"And there simply hasn't been a trans-temporal interference of this order before!" Don Miguel rubbed his weary eyes. "There hasn't even been a temporal feedback process worth mentioning, apart from—"

He stopped dead in mid-sentence, and stared at Father Ramón. After a pregnant pause, he said, "Father, I have an idea. I don't know if it will work, but at least it would mean our interfering where there's already been a disturbance of the time-line."

A gleam of hope appeared in Father Ramón's sharp eyes. "Tell me, then!" he commanded.

"The Mass, Father, Could we not take advantage of the Society's New Year Mass?"

For a long moment Father Ramón stared. Then, unexpectedly, he burst into a crow of laughter.

"Of course—the Mass! My blessings on you, my son! That I could have been so blind as to overlook the Mass!"

SEVEN

As the outline of a familiar room took shape around him, Don Miguel at long last dared to relax. There was no mistaking one of the robing-cells in the antesection to the chapel of the Society, nor the sound of the high clear bell which was tolling somewhere outside.

He was here.

But was he—*now*?

There was as yet no possible means of answering that question. His ordeal was still a long way from being over. He knew as well as Father Ramón himself that he was part of a terrifying experiment, an operation such as no one in history had ever dared to conduct before, and the implications were impossible to foresee.

Dutifully, as the Jesuit had directed, he had done his best to work them out. He had been given a computation to analyse in factors which Father Ramón had hastily scribbled down, and aided by a shy, precocious junior Probationer, aged only about seventeen but possessed of a remarkable gift for mathematics, he had struggled through to a solution. He tried as he worked to assign real-world values to the symbols, and thought that most likely he must be dealing with labels for human lives, for one by one he saw them cancel out, cancel out . . .

The problem reduced to an undefined variable and a factor k, and he showed this result to Father Ramón, who stared at it for a long time before he sighed, closed his eyes for an instant as though formulating a prayer, and then bade him go up to the time-halls in the central tower.

There, under the direction of white-faced, anxious technicians—what few they had been able to assemble from their homes—he took station between the familiar iron and silver bars. There was an intolerable period of waiting while settings were checked, re-checked and double-checked, but he endured it. He realised that he was about to be sent on such a voyage as the Society had never before attempted. Upon his departure, he would wipe out a whole abortive branch of reality.

Suddenly the air grew very hot—

—and he was here in a robing-cell of the chapel, and the bell above was tolling as it had done each New Year's Eve since the Society acquired this palace as the official residence of its Commander.

His mind raced, wondering what the significance had been of that factor k. Was it the King, perhaps, whose life or death could more radically alter reality than that of a commoner? Modesty argued for it. But he suspected that in truth the person represented was himself, whom Kristina's whim had saved from the holocaust at the palace.

And who now had to repay that gift of Providence, with interest.

He recognised, of course, the necessity of undoing what had been done. If left to stand unaltered, the consequences of this night of madness would be a blot forever on the records of the Society. Moreover, the death of the King and all his nearest heirs, and the Ambassador of the Confederacy and other ambassadors and so many of the nobility and gentry of the Empire, was an effect utterly disproportionate to the act.

Yet even after ploughing through all the texts Father Ramón had selected for him he knew only one thing for sure about the effects of setting up a closed causative loop: no one could possibly predict the outcome.

His mind swirled like water in a rotating cup. Putting his hands to his head, he struggled to think coherently. He had been trained to some extent in casuistry, and he could see the dim outlines of a logical sequence such as must have persuaded Father Ramón to take his unprecedented gamble. Postulate: the terrible women gladiators who wrought the harm originated in a non-actual world—a world brought about by the experimental interference of Society explorers with their own recorded history. Therefore the consequences of their acts might also be regarded as non-actual, or potential. Therefore the rectification of those consequences would be *not* non-actual, if this was a safe case to exclude the middle ...

It occurred to him with blinding suddenness that unless something had gone hideously wrong all the nightmare in his memory had *already not happened*.

For a moment he had a glimpse of what it must be like to be a man such as Father Ramón, all his mind lighted by a logic as piercing as sunlight, driven by a terrible, inexorable honesty to conceal nothing from himself. And he felt sweat prickle all over his body as he realised that here, now, in the rectified situation he was the possessor of a unique personal past.

Briefly, the awareness of that paralysed him. He thought his very heart would stop; he could imagine himself dying with the shock, especially when the tolling of the bell abruptly ceased to strike his ears. Then, from the passage beyond the door of his robing-cell, he discerned the slow shuffling sound of feet, and realised the bell had stopped in . . . *reality*.

If the word any longer meant anything.

Either way, the Society was assembling for New Year Mass, for the most awful of all its formal occasions, and he would have to join the congregation. He calmed himself deliberately with deep breathing. When finally he decided he could walk without swaying, he took his own enveloping robe from the wall, slipped it on, and pulled the hood far forward over his face. Then he opened the cell door and hastened in the wake of his colleagues.

These, tonight, were all faceless men. Only differences of height and girth could give the slightest clue to their identity: the hoods hid their features, the sleeves hid their hands, the robes fell to the ground and swished around their feet. For a reason. For the reason which only members of the Society knew, and which made this Mass the unique occasion it was.

Grey into the grey shadows of the chapel, lit only by two candles at the east end, whose thin beams played fitfully on the gilded coats of arms mounted over the officers' stalls but were too faint to reveal the faces of the company one to another. To the solemn music of the organ the company dispersed among the pews.

Now, this year, there were eight hundred and forty-six

Probationers, Licentiates and Officers of the Society. Accordingly the pews held eight hundred and forty-six grey-garbed men.

And any one of them might not be a present member, but someone who was doomed to die in the Society's service.

Only the officiating priest, bringing the Host to the row of kneeling brothers, would be able to see by the light of the altar candles whether one of the worshippers was a stranger, and thus tell which of the present members—here words were lacking—was *tonight* celebrating the Mass with his colleagues of an age yet to come.

And the priest was masked.

In his stall, Don Miguel thought of everything which that knowledge implied. He—after all, he himself—might not in fact be at the Mass of the New Year's Eve he had so far been living through. Every year the organ played the same music; every year a Papal dispensation was given to conduct the service in whispers, so that any stranger in their midst might not recognise the priest's voice as unfamiliar and thereby gain foreknowledge of approaching death. One might of course count the grey robes present to see if the total differed from what he expected—

Don Miguel glanced round into the shadows, and shook his head. No. No man would do that. No man would dare.

There was a shuffling. The grey robes rose, and the masked priest came forth before the altar

EIGHT

By the time the service was over, he had worked out what he must now do. He filed out of the chapel with the rest of the Society and returned to his robing-cell. The purpose of isolating the members from each other for a few minutes before and after the service, of course, was not merely to afford them a chance for a moment of private meditation; it was also to facilitate the transfer from this time-location of whoever had been selected to partake of a New Year's Mass in a future age, and his subsequent return. There was never any way of detecting the process.

But, of course, it was only convenient to operate the transfer from a robing-cell. It wasn't necessary.

And tonight, if he had reached the correct conclusion, an exception would have been made. He was virtually certain he knew whom it had affected.

A kind of grim excitement began to displace his former

apprehension as he stripped off his robes. He barely spared time to hang it tidily on its peg before leaving the cell—ahead of most of his colleagues, who were doubtless spending a while in prayer before returning to the reception at the palace.

Following a cold, stone-flagged passage, he passed the chapel and made for the vestry at the other end. Hurrying more and more, against his will, his heels clicking on the floor, he came at last to the door which was his destination. There he halted. Shivers traced down his spine.

Suppose—just suppose—some unforeseeable error had nullified the plan; suppose, when he knocked, it was another voice than Father Ramón's that invited him to enter!

Well, there was only one way to find out. He raised his fist to hammer on the wood, and his heart pounded in answer as he recognised that it was indeed Father Ramón who was within.

He twisted the handle and stepped over the threshold.

The Jesuit was alone in the starkly furnished little room, standing close to a table with one thin hand laid on its polished top, his eyes bright and sharp in his bird-like face. On recognising his visitor he smiled.

"A fortunate new year to you, my son," he said. "It's kind of you to come calling when the year is still so young. I'd have thought you'd be eager to return to the merrymaking in the palace—" He broke off, searching Don Miguel's face, and resumed in a more serious tone.

"Forgive me for jesting!" he exclaimed. "For I see by your expression you're here on no light errand."

"Truth, Father—I'm afraid. And so strange an errand, too, that I'm at a loss to know how to convince you I'm neither drunk nor dreaming." Don Miguel passed his tongue over dry lips. "I think, though, you may take me seriously if I say that I know which of our present-day company was absent from the Mass tonight."

The smile vanished from Father Ramón's face. He said, "That's hardly a matter for casual chat, my son. You had indeed better satisfy me of your grounds for mentioning it."

"I'll try." Don Miguel swallowed hard. "You'll grant there's no normal means I could find out by? You'll take my word that I haven't pried into any secret records—that I don't even know for certain such records exist?"

"You puzzle me . . . But I'll accept your word. Continue."

"How then can I be positive that the present-day Licentiate you did not serve at tonight's Mass was—Don Arturo Cortés?"

There was a long pause. Father Ramón terminated it by reaching for a black-bound book from a shelf at his side. On its front cover it bore a cross embossed in gold. He set it on the table between them and nodded for Don Miguel to sit down. Doing so, the latter laid one hand on the book and with the other wiped perspiration from his forehead.

"There's something else I'm giving you my word about, Father," he resumed. "I've never—in this world as it is— entered the restricted room of the library. But I know, and you know, that at the court of King Mahendra the White Elephant they have female gladiators who fight like Hash-ishin."

"You learned of them from Don Arturo?" snapped Father Ramón.

"No, I've never spoken to him about it. You must know there's little love lost between him and me."

"Then who—?"

"You yourself, Father. You told me about them."

Once more there was a terrible silence. In the light of the lamps the Jesuit's face gleamed like oiled parchment. But his voice was quite level as he said, "You speak in riddles, yet you have not the air of a madman. I must hear you out. Go on."

"You told me so that I could tell you now, in my turn, and so convince you I'm not out of my mind. You made me party to a secret which would gain your own attention."

"In that you've succeeded," admitted the Jesuit. "For good and sufficient reasons the existence of this potential world you've mentioned has never been advertised. Perhaps you can imagine why?"

"Because in that world the true faith is suppressed?" ventured Don Miguel.

"Correct. And there are other reasons, but that's the chief. So explain your version of events."

Already, Don Miguel realised, his fantastic mind must have touched the kernel of the matter. Already he must be aware that he was condemned to the worst of all possible human predicaments: to judge actions of his own that he had no knowledge of . . .

Aloud, he said, "First, Father, you must write a message to the future. To ensure the security of our very world, you must issue instructions—unquestionable orders, under the Great Seal of the Society—that when the day comes that Don Arturo is sent to celebrate Mass with the brothers of another time than his own, he must be fetched from an earlier time than usual. He must lose, as nearly as I can judge, three whole hours from his evening. Above all, he must not be allowed to speak with the Ambassador of the Confederacy or anyone else concerning the subject of women as valiant fighters."

Father Ramón looked stricken. He said. "I will do as you

ask. But tell me why."

So, by pieces and scraps, Don Miguel did so.

When he had finished, Father Ramón sat for a long while in silence. At last he stirred, his face perfectly white.

He said, "Yes. Yes, it could have happened. A venal and corrupt mind panders to the whim of a monarch—and the result is the slaughter of thousands. You have performed a signal service to the Society, my son. But no doubt you understand that your only reward must be a dreadful nightmare of knowledge."

Don Miguel nodded. His voice thick, he said, "Worse yet than the knowledge is my present ignorance! I feel like a leaf tossed on the wind. Do I know what I have done—now in this world—during the evening that's passed?"

"With caution and grace you'll establish that before any harm results," Father Ramón promised. "But . . . Well, do you wish to be free of what you know? I can release you if you prefer—what you remember is now clearly non-existent, and it would be lawful to banish it from your brain."

Don Miguel hesitated. The idea was tempting, and he knew the process nowadays would be quick and easy—there were humane drugs developed by the Holy Office for the relief of sincerely repentant criminals whose guilt-feelings prevented them from becoming useful members of society.

But suddenly he said, amazed at himself, "No, Father. For you know what I know now. And I feel it would somehow be unjust to leave you in sole possession of this knowledge, sharing it with no one else."

"It is shared with God," the Jesuit reminded him gently. "But—I thank you, nonetheless. It seems to me a brave thing to say." He drew back the book stamped with the cross and held it before him in both hands.

"I counsel you now, for your peace of mind, to return to the palace reception. The longer you allow this memory of what did not happen to dominate your mind, the longer you'll be ill at ease. Go back and see for yourself that the palace stands unburned, that the King lives, that your friend Don Felipe has not been shot full of arrows. In the end it will become like a dream."

"Was it in truth nothing more?" Don Miguel insisted. Father Ramón gave a skeletal smile.

"Tomorrow—later today, rather, if you wish, come to me and I will recommend you some texts in the library which treat of the powers and limitations of the Adversary. It is possible for him to create convincing delusions, but not to create reality. And it is always possible for determined and upright men to penetrate those delusions."

He rose to his feet. Don Miguel did the same, then dropped to his knees and bowed his head. When the priest had blessed him, he looked up.

"And you, Father? What are you going to do?"

"Write the message to the future, as you directed. Review certain undesirable elements of vanity in the character of a prominent Licentiate. Perhaps draft a scare-mongering article for publication in one of the Society's journals, which no one will dare to dismiss as absurd thanks to my not inconsiderable reputation. And also, of course, I shall pray."

He walked past Don Miguel and opened the door.

"Go with God, my son," he said.

NINE

His mind churning, Don Miguel walked slowly along the cold passage which connected the chapel to the adjacent palace. He could hear the sound of the band performing again, and voices singing with it, and much laughter.

This was real.

Yet—how *much* of what had happened to him had happened to no one else? Had he spent this evening in Londres with Kristina, mingling with the crowds? Clearly they had not encountered the feathered girl at Empire Circle, but what had they done instead?

Was he in fact already at the reception?

That final shocking possibility stopped him in his tracks. With a shake of his head he dismissed it. If not before now, then later, under the direction of Father Ramón, the Society would take/have taken steps to rectify any such paradox. He could clearly recall the precautions which the technicians at the Headquarters Office had (not) carried out to ensure he arrived within a minute or two of midnight in this rectified reality. But he had overlapped with himself in one sense, of course, because in the potential world at the corresponding moment to this he had been with Father Ramón and Kristina at the Headquarters Office, and here he was rejoining the party instead . . .

Wrestling with the insoluble problem threatened to give him a headache. He snatched his attention back to his surroundings and realised that he was now in a warm, well-lit, gaily-decorated corridor; he had regained the interior of the palace. Any moment now he might emerge into a room full of guests and find Kristina impatiently awaiting him on his return from the Mass.

Or—his heart sank at the prospect—he might learn that she and he had not slipped away together to the city, but had spent a miserably dull evening making polite small-talk until she lost patience with him and found an excuse to choose herself a livelier partner.

Father Ramón had counselled him to proceed with grace and caution. The former he could not control, but he could certainly abide by the latter. Instead of making directly for the main hall where the body of the party was, he turned aside down another corridor where slaves were coming and going with the traditional New Year breakfast on trays and trolleys, and bowls of steaming mulled wine giving off a spicy aroma. This led him to a sheltered alcove from which he could spy out the land before showing himself.

By now the great hall was half as full as before. There was no sign of the King, but at least one might presume he'd departed peacefully. Likewise there was no sign of the Ambassador of the Confederacy. But he spotted the Prince

Imperial, having a whale of a time with a pretty Mohawk girl just in front of the bandstand, and there too was Red Bear slumped down in a chair and holding court. He'd probably had to be sobered up forcibly to take part in the Mass; imagine a Licentiate trying to get away with that, but of course a General Officer—

"Miguel!"

He glanced round, startled. Coming towards him, smiling broadly, was Don Felipe.

"Miguel, where've *you* been all evening?" He gave his friend a poke in the ribs and a knowing wink. "Don't tell me, let me guess—only I'd better not say *what* I guess! I'm sure you've been enjoying yourself anyway."

"Yes!" Don Miguel seized on the slim clue, "Have you been looking for me, then?"

"Not especially," Don Felipe chortled. "I've had—ah—other things to occupy me. But I did notice you were conspicuous by your absence."

"Then perhaps you'd better put me in the picture about what's been going on," Don Miguel suggested, trying to adopt a blasé tone. "I—ah—might have to cover my absence, mightn't I?"

Don Felipe's eyes grew round as O's. "Miguel, you don't mean . . . ? Why, you lucky so-and-so! Ingeborg's tremendous fun, but she's a little on the young side for—"

"Felipe!" Don Miguel interrupted sharply.

"All right, all right!" Don Felipe parodied repentance. "Never take a lady's name in vain, and all that pow-wow . . . Well, make it snappy; I'm in a hurry to get rid of the drink I've had and get back to Ingeborg. Where did you lose touch?"

"Uh . . ." Don Miguel frowned. "Wasn't there some kind of

a disagreement between the royals and the Ambassador of the Confederacy?"

"Oh, that! Yes, it was pretty stormy for a while—Red Bear was still in fair possession of his faculties and rounded up a bunch of us to try and provide a distraction. But it didn't help much, largely because your old chum the Marquesa di Jorque kept starting all kinds of irrelevant hares. In fact at one point it nearly came to a free fight about women's rights. The real fly in the ointment, though, was Don Arturo, as you might expect. Luckily for everyone he got mislaid at some stage. Drank too much, I shouldn't wonder. Good Lord! Glutton for punishment, isn't he? He's over there—see?—and isn't he just knocking it back!"

Don Miguel glanced in the direction Don Felipe indicated, and there indeed was Don Arturo, pale as a ghost and trying apparently to restore his colour by gulping glass after glass of red wine.

"So what happened after that?" Don Miguel said slowly.

"Oh, the subject got changed to something less controversial and when the royals left about half past eleven and the Ambassador too there was laughing all round and hand-shaking and all kinds of friendliness. Perfectly calm and in order. Miguel, forgive me but I *must* disappear!"

He vanished down the corridor, leaving Don Miguel to sigh with relief. It really was all right, then. The only point which did still briefly puzzle him was this: if the doyen of the diplomatic corps, the Ambassador from the Confederacy, had left before midnight, it would presumably have been to celebrate Mass at the embassy, and the rest of the foreign dignitaries would have done the same. So why had Ingeborg remained—would she have stayed later than her father?

Then he remembered that, being of a heterodox faith, the

Scandinavians probably had different observances. In which case he stood an excellent chance of locating Kristina and finding that they had indeed spent those delightful few hours playing truant from the party. He was about to set off happily in search of her when he glanced again in the direction of Don Arturo.

No, there was one thing he must attend to before going to look for Kristina. It was little enough to do for a man —likeable or detestable—who had suffered one of the cruellest fates imaginable for anyone. He must realise that he had lost part of his evening; he must know it was due to no such commonplace cause as drinking himself into a stupor; logically, then, he must be the first (*and may he be the only!*— added Don Miguel's mind silently) member of the Society to realise that he was not celebrating the New Year Mass in his own time.

What justice was there in allowing him to suffer now that the consequences of his heedless boasting had been swept into limbo?

Well, that was a matter to be left to the casuists, if they ever learned about it. He was not, at least, as badly off as Father Ramón, who must judge his own actions without having committed them. But he must be in an agony of apprehension.

Don Miguel strode across the floor, his heart abrim with sudden pity, and halted before Don Arturo. "Your hand, brother!" he exclaimed. "Let me wish you a happy new year!"

For an instant Don Arturo's haunted eyes locked with his and he seemed not to understand the words. Then, convulsively, he let fall his wineglass with a crash and seized Don Miguel's hand in both of his. He said nothing, but his smile was bright.

A prompt slave came to snatch up the fragments of glass and wipe away the wasted wine. Drawing back from Don Arturo's grip, Don Miguel heard his name called in a familiar voice.

"Ah, there you are, Miguel! What's kept you so long?"

Only a few paces distant around the floor, there was Kristina standing between her father and her sister, vigorously waving to him. His heart turned over, and he hastened to comply with her beckoning. After a rapid bow to the Duke, he addressed her.

"I'm so sorry, Lady Kristina. I've been—ah—having a few words with Father Ramón in his vestry."

She looked slightly puzzled at his use of her title, and then seemed to hit on an explanation. "Oh, Papa doesn't mind people calling me Kristina, Miguel, if that's what you're thinking. He's just had to get used to it—haven't you?" she added, nudging her father playfully.

The Duke of Scania chuckled. "Indeed I have," he admitted. "I've even had to put up with her so-called progressive friends addressing me as 'Duke' pure and simple. Well, I never cared much for starchy formalities myself." He looked quizzically at Don Miguel. "I take it you and my daughter have been getting on all right—at any rate, I've hardly seen either of you all the evening."

Kristina bubbled mischievously. "Miguel's been wonderful, Papa! We got dreadfully bored, so he found a way for us to slip out, and we've been all around the city mixing with the people and having a marvellous time. You'd never think it to look at him, but he's got quite a sense of humour behind that grim scarred face. Of course, Miguel, I suppose because you're really very stern the reason you wanted to see Father Ramón was to confess how wicked you'd been this evening—

escorting an unchaperoned girl!"

"Kristina!" the Duke said reprovingly. "How often must I tell you? You don't make jokes about other people's religious belief!"

A sort of strange light-headedness was overcoming Don Miguel now. Already the gruesome events he had thought to be indelibly engraved on his memory were receding, becoming unreal, fading as chalk-marks fade under a wet sponge until the words are as though they had never been written. He said, "Heavens, no, Kristina! I could never regret enjoying an evening with you. Let me prove it by asking you for another dance, and this time I hope it won't be rudely cut short like the first."

He bowed his leave of the Duke and led her out on the floor. Taking her hand, he murmured to himself, "Everything for the best in the best of all possible worlds."

"What was that, Miguel? I didn't quite catch—"

"Nothing. Just a rather bitter anti-clerical joke. It doesn't matter."

"Oh, explain it!" she urged.

A look of sadness passing over his face, he shook his head. "Believe me, Kristina, I couldn't. Nobody could. Forget it, and let's just dance."

PART III

THE FULLNESS OF TIME

ONE

"Your people," said the long-faced Mohawk who managed the mines, "came to what you call the New World hungry for gold. You came looking for fabulous kingdoms—Cibola, Quivira, Norumbega, Texas. And so keenly were you disappointed when you found they didn't exist, you set about creating them."

He waved at the hillside opposite, where the mine galleries ran like holes into ripe cheese. Don Miguel followed the gesture with his eyes. Here where he sat with the manager—whose name was Two Dogs—it was cool under the shadow of woven reed awnings, on the verandah of the plain mud-plastered house which served as both home and administrative offices. But there the fury of the sun lay full, and the Indian labourers emerging from the mouths of the galleries with their baskets full of crushed rock, to be tipped into sluices for sedimentation, wiped their dusty faces, swigged water from leathern bottles, and seemed glad to escape underground again.

The heat of the air was such that the world felt silent, although there were always noises: the monotonous creaking of the pumps bringing up water for the sluices, the droning of flies, the cries of the overseers in a local dialect that Don Miguel did not understand. But taken together they constituted no more of an irritation than birdsong. Half a world away from home, Don Miguel was contentedly able to relax.

"More wine?" Two Dogs suggested, raising the jug from the table between them.

"Willingly," Don Miguel returned, holding out his glass. "It's very good. You grow the grapes locally, I understand."

Two Dogs nodded, pouring for his visitor and himself. "Our climate here in California is very good for vines. This cheese also is local—take a piece. The flavours mingle well." He set down the jug and offered a large baked-clay platter on which a wedge of yellow cheese stood, stuck with a silver knife.

"Speaking of which," he continued, "the very name of California is an instance of what I mean. Am I not correct in saying that it commemorates the legend of a non-existent queen named Calaf, whom your early explorers fondly believed to rule over an island populated exclusively by women?"

"I've heard some such tale," Don Miguel agreed, and tried a crumb of the cheese; finding it to his liking, he cut a piece as big as his palm and bit into its edge. "Indeed, I seem to recall that there was opposition to the adoption of that name for this province on the grounds that 'California' was notoriously mythical and no one would wish to emigrate and settle in a place that didn't exist."

He chuckled. To his surprise, he realised after a moment that Two Dogs looked the reverse of amused, and broke off, hoping he had not committed a major social gaffe. Apart from the very much Europeanised Mohawks whom he had met in Londres and New Madrid, he had made the acquaintance of hardly any Indians, and here—three thousand miles further west on the American continent than he had ever travelled before—he was only sketchily informed concerning customs, etiquette and formal behaviour. Of course, dealing as he did with traders and industrial middlemen from the east Two Dogs must be used to foreign manners in his guests, but there was no point in imposing on his goodwill. Don Miguel counted himself lucky to have run across him—he was an interesting talker and surprisingly widely read in view of his rather humdrum profession.

He said now, "In that case we can be grateful that the name was selected. Perhaps that's what kept down the number of immigrants to a level we can tolerate . . . after a fashion."

"Do you not have many European residents hereabouts?" Don Miguel asked.

"A handful." Two Dogs shrugged. "Some of whom one is compelled to put up with, such as the priests; some of whom are acceptably useful in the community, such as our two doctors—one of them more than the other, because he's prepared to listen to what we can tell him about our local herbs and medicinal plants while the other won't pay attention to any remedy not vouched for by a journal from Londres with the *Imprimatur* on it! And a few others most of whom do your people no credit: several are dishonest and many of them are drunkards."

Don Miguel stirred uneasily in his chair. He said, "Well, of course, from the point of view of you Mohawks, we must seem—"

"Correction," interrupted Two Dogs with a thin-lipped smile. He was a very striking man to look at, taller than Don Miguel and with a rangy leanness that made his visitor think of a fast racehorse. "I'm only by courtesy a Mohawk—about an eighth of my ancestry, as near as I can work out. The rest is mostly Sioux, Apache and Paiute. And that's another thing which annoys me about you Imperials. For example, take your own case. You bear a Spanish name, you speak a variety of Spanish rather heavily salted with English, French and even some Dutch phrases—but are you *Spanish?*"

"I see what you mean," admitted Don Miguel. "I am mostly Spanish, but my father's mother was French and my mother's mother was half-English. Which is presumably why one talks about Imperials rather than Spaniards nowadays—apart from the fact that we were displaced from our homeland, remember."

"And are you the only ones?" Two Dogs sighed. "You talk of me as Mohawk. Look at a map. Mohawks of a pure strain can be found only some two and a half thousand miles to the east of where we're sitting. The rest are diluted across the continent thanks to the mere accident which resulted in your cementing an alliance with them and giving them the necessary horses and guns to set forth on a wave of conquest. It could as easily have been—oh—their neighbours the Mohicans, couldn't it?"

Something seemed to sound a warning bell in Don Miguel's mind. Was it pure coincidence that Two Dogs had put that hypothesis to him, a time-traveller who might give an authoritative answer?

It must be! No one for a thousand miles was supposed to know the identity of this visitor from Londres. That was the whole point of coming so far for his furlough—to get away, even if only for a month or so, from the oppressive demands of his job and the nightmarish recollection of what a single error could do to the fabric of reality.

Damn Two Dogs, anyway. The last thing Don Miguel wanted to think about right now was the question of speculative time. Since the appearance of Father Ramón's recent article, "An Analysis of the Probable Implications of Cross-Temporal Human Contact", no one at the Headquarters Office seemed to have talked about any other subject, and with his own unsharable burden of secret knowledge Don Miguel was unable to enter into argument with the enthusiasm practically all his colleagues displayed.

But . . . Well, yes, it could have been the Mohicans instead of the Mohawks. Very easily. If Chief Tallfeather had been killed in the Battle of Twin Creek instead of Chief Storm, the latter—who was nearly as brilliant a strategist—would almost certainly have received the crucial embassy from the Governor of New Madrid. And from then on things would have continued in pretty much the same fashion.

I might even be here, now, being told off for calling some quasi-counterpart of Two Dogs a Mohican when he was actually Comanche, Pima and Shoshone!

Determinedly he drove the subject from his mind. He was sick of it, and what he'd been through last New Year was still giving him nightmares months afterwards. He made a vain attempt to turn the conversation by asking about the miners across the valley, but Two Dogs was equally set on sticking to the subject . . . and, being the host, won thanks to Don Miguel's desire not to cause offence.

"It was, of course, in one sense at least a fortunate accident. One need only look south past the Isthmus to see what the alternative might have been—hm?"

Embarrassed, Don Miguel cast around for a neutral reply. It was always upsetting for an Imperial citizen to be reminded of the fate of the great civilisations of Central and South America, sacrificed on the altar of European greed. He said at last, "There has never been change without suffering—it's the way of the world, I'm afraid."

"And as you people saw it, it might as well be the provincials who suffered," suggested Two Dogs. "You spoke a moment ago of emigrants who might decide not to come here because the name you'd given the area suggested that it didn't exist. I find myself tempted to enquire: what emigrants? Are they emigrants who are crouching and sweating in the mine galleries yonder? Or are they natives, dispossessed from their old hunting-grounds and compelled to adopt this miserable means of earning their living?"

What have I stumbled across—some revanchist fanatic? Don Miguel was tempted to revise his opinion of Two Dogs from start to finish on that basis alone. But he held his peace, and cut another slice of cheese.

"As I see it," the mine manager pursued, "you conceive of yourselves as looking from the centre outwards. Europe is the heart of the world and the other continents are—what would one call them?—its outskirts, perhaps. Of course, in one way that's become a self-fulfilling prophecy; at least, over the past five hundred years, a great many local squabbles in Europe have created changes out of all proportion here, in Africa and in Asia. It's taught people like me to be grateful for small mercies. We don't seem to have had any big ones for quite a while."

The words dug into Don Miguel's mind like the touch of an eagle's claw. Feeling little premonitory tinglings on the nape of his neck, he said, "I'm not entirely certain that I follow you."

"Don't you? Well, here's an example of what I'd call a small mercy. Suppose your Empire hadn't won its greatest victory. Suppose there hadn't been a strong power in Western Europe in the seventeenth and eighteenth centuries, and—like Eastern Europe—the area had split into petty principalities, because you'd lost the Netherlands before you could use them as a launching-site for your invasion of England, and when the Moors reconquered Spain you had nowhere to go. Wouldn't we Indians then have had four or more gangs of Europeans fighting over our hunting-grounds like dogs over a bone?"

Don Miguel was by this time convinced that he was being needled. In a last desperate effort to prove that his identity was not suspected, he said, "It's an interesting argument. Obviously you've made a study of history."

"So have you," Two Dogs said, and looked him straight in the eye. "You are a Licentiate of the Society of Time, aren't you?"

TWO

Don Miguel uttered a long succession of colourful curses in the next few seconds—but under his breath. Finally, he reached for the wine-jug and refilled his glass without asking permission. Not looking at the other, he said, "Can't I get away from it *anywhere?*"

"What do you mean?"

"I came to California for a rest. Simply for a rest! I got so sick at home of being shown off like a circus animal—looky looky, here's a time-traveller, let's make him do some tricks to amuse us! How in the name of all that's holy did you find out?"

Two Dogs gave a dry chuckle, "*I* see. With your typically European parochialism, you thought that this was the end of the world. Well, it's true we're a long way from Londres, but that doesn't mean that we don't hear the news eventually. On your way to California you passed through New Madrid. The

Prince of New Castile, who's the Commander of your Society,
happened to be in residence at his palace there, making one of
his infrequent visits to the territory he nominally governs. You
called on him to pay your respects. And . . ." An expressive
shrug. "There can't be very many people in the world by the
name of Miguel Navarro."

"By the infernal fires, isn't there anywhere on Earth I can
get away from it all?" Don Miguel, scowling terribly so that
the cicatrised sword-slash on his cheek nearly vanished as the
muscles under it tightened, slapped his open palm on the
table in an access of fury.

"Away from what?"

"I told you! From these sensation-seekers who always seem
to descend on a time-traveller like flies on rotten meat—and
they're no less unwholesome, I tell you straight!"

"Well, that at least I can promise you you'll be spared,"
Two Dogs said. "Our code of good behaviour doesn't allow us
to offend visitors in that fashion. In fact, out of deference to
your wish for anonymity, I'd drop the subject but for one
thing."

"That being . . . ?"

"By now, Don Miguel, there isn't anywhere on Earth
you—I mean Europeans generally—can 'get away from it all.'
You've scarred the face of the planet far too deeply. They tell
me that even the sterile snow of the South Pole is now littered
with the refuse of the explorers you've sent to it."

There was a pause, and Don Miguel again stared across the
valley towards the mines. Honesty compelled him to accept,
watching the half-naked workers there whose brown skins
were turned nearly yellow by the coating of mineral dust they
wore, that in the fierce summer heat they must be suffering

torments of thirst and weariness. Yes, it was regrettable, but true: the greed of Europe had caused a lot of harm to people who didn't deserve it.

He sighed, and drained his glass. This time Two Dogs filled it anew.

"And there's another more personal reason for not acting as I suppose I ought to," he went on meditatively. "I am, as you deduced, very much interested in history. To forego this chance to talk with an expert from the centre of world affairs is something I'll only do if you're insistent."

"As you like," Don Miguel conceded, comforting himself with the reflection that—judging by what Two Dogs had so far said—questions from him would be on a higher level than those from, say, the Marquesa di Jorque.

"You're kind," Two Dogs said formally. "In the event, let me ask if you agree with the proposition I advanced a short time ago. Is it not probable that without Imperial dominance over the nearer coast of Europe, and your virtual monopoly of trans-Atlantic sea-trade, we'd likely have had you, and the French, and the Swedes, and the Dutch, and even the English, transporting their local differences to this continent and battling over them? And we poor Indians might have been ground between them like corn between millstones."

There could be no doubt that he took his hypothesis seriously; under the shadow of the reed awning his face was as grim and ominous as one of the idols carved by his Central American cousins. Don Miguel marvelled at the change which had overtaken him, and wished achingly that it could have been any other subject than this which had arisen between them. He had taken quite a liking to Two Dogs since their first meeting three days earlier, and had looked forward to a lot of idle small-talk to distract his mind from the things that preyed on it.

But here, now, Two Dogs had gone to the core of his anxieties as directly as a skilled engineer sinking a mineshaft to a lode of ore.

Well, there was no help for it. But tomorrow or some time soon he'd be advised to move on to some even more remote townlet, possibly even register at an inn under an assumed name . . .

With yet another sigh, the deepest of all, he said, "Oh . . . Yes, I suppose it's possible. Though personally I doubt whether any would-be conqueror with so small an economic base as a single member-country of the Empire—even France, which is relatively large and fairly wealthy—could have established a permanent bridgehead here if the Indians had united to oppose them."

"Oh, I think so," contradicted Two Dogs. "I think what you would have done would be to take advantage of our poor internal communications and the linguistic distinctions which divided us. Some of us might have been tempted to throw in our lot with one party, some with another, until in the end we were as war-torn and antagonistic as you."

"You have an excessively cynical attitude towards Europeans," Don Miguel objected mildly.

"I contest that. Reverting for a moment to the role you've enforced on me, and thinking in Mohawk terms: was it not a cynical action to single out one small tribe among so many and equip it to embark on a grand crusade clear to the Pacific? That's how we learned to be cynical, if there's any truth in your charge! Not that I'm admitting the term is justified. It's more that being allied with the Empire is like being brother to a hot-headed adventurer. Any day a feud in which he's embroiled himself may explode in the face of his family without their knowledge or desire."

Thinking of the currently strained relations between the Empire and its coeval super-power the Confederacy of the East—and, still more alarming, of the recent rumours that westernised scientists in Cathay were on the track of time apparatus of their own, which might lead to who could guess what consequences in view of the widespread Oriental belief that the material world was *maya*, illusory!—Don Miguel was compelled to give a nod of acquiescence.

"It is mainly because of that," Two Dogs added after a pause, "that I'm infringing our code of good manners. It's disquieting to learn that a supposedly innocent tourist, here to rest and relax in the California sunlight, is actually a time-traveller. Particularly in view of . . ."

"What?" Don Miguel, alerted by he could not say what reaction of his subconscious, made the word crackle like a firearrow.

For a long moment Two Dogs seemed to be struggling towards a decision. Suddenly he drained his wine-glass and slammed it down hard on the table.

"I'll show you! Because—though it shames me to admit it to a foreigner—what I'm talking about is too much for one man to endure knowledge of by himself!"

Without further explanation he jumped to his feet and strode down the hillside shouting at the top of his lungs for Tomás, his dour chief overseer. Some of the labourers on the far side of the valley heard, paused in their work and looked to see what madness had come over their master. More slowly, Don Miguel followed him, screwing up his eyes with the shock of the strong sunlight. By the time he caught up with Two Dogs he had located Tomás and was giving him orders in the incomprehensible local Indian language. He ventured to ask

what the sudden fuss was all about, but the only answer he got
was, "Wait and see!"

Much puzzled, indeed greatly disturbed, Don Miguel was
forced to contain himself while Tomas went in search of two
burros with saddles fit for gentlefolk. The sketchy outline of a
pattern was forming in his mind, and the ingredients that
made it up were alarming. Clearly it had been his admission
that he was a member of the Society of Time which triggered
the Mohawk's outburst—but what possible connection could
there be between the arrival of a Licentiate of the Society in
this back-of-beyond community, and the sudden trans-
formation of a mine manager into a man apparently struck
into a frenzy of panic?

After a wait of only a few minutes—which felt to Don
Miguel like a miniature foretaste of eternity—Tomás returned with their mounts. Then, wrapping his old but bright
serape around him, he set forth ahead of them along a narrow
dusty trail, walking steadily with the aid of a staff.

Don Miguel decided after the first twenty yards that he too
would rather be on foot. The jogging of the burro was so
unlike the motion of a horse as to make him uncomfortable.
Besides, it was nearing the middle of the day and the flies
were troublesome; he would have preferred to have both
hands free to swat at them. But a glance at Two Dogs
persuaded him not to mention these facts. The Mohawk wore
the expression of a man driven by demons.

The trail wound over the shoulder of the hill, becoming in
places a mere footpath, but the burros were at least sure-
footed and Tomás marched ahead stolidly. Once past the
hillcrest, beyond the limit of the land that the miners had so
far attacked, a smaller valley lay baking in the sun. Only the
trail winding across it suggested that men had ever disturbed

it. That apart, it might have lain as it was since Creation Day.

"There!" Two Dogs said, causing his burro to fall back alongside Don Miguel's. He raised his arm and pointed to a rocky slope ahead.

After careful scrutiny, Don Miguel said, "I'm afraid I see nothing out of the ordinary."

"Well, then, come and look more closely," Two Dogs grunted, and kicked his mount into a reluctant trot.

What in the world could have so shattered the man's normal Mohawk imperturbability?

It appeared that Tomás also knew what they were heading for; he turned aside and scrambled straight up a steep rocky incline, while Two Dogs on his burro had to take a more roundabout route. Abandoning the animal to wander, he jumped down at the overseer's side and the two of them together leaned against a large round boulder, nearly man-high, about which at first glance Don Miguel saw nothing remarkable.

Then, as they strained against it, it rocked back and forth. Suddenly it gave, rolling through half a circle and coming to rest in a cup of ground which fitted it so accurately it could scarcely have been accidental. Its displacement revealed an opening in the slope behind. A dark, roughly square opening. The mouth of a tunnel.

The mouth of the gallery of a mine!

Don Miguel felt horrified understanding dawn. Hastening to join the others, he stared down the black tunnel—seeing nothing because of the contrast with the bright sun—and demanded, "What is this? I didn't think you'd begun to mine this valley!"

"We haven't," Two Dogs confirmed. He seemed to have recovered his habitual self-possession, and his tone was sardonic. "But there doesn't seem to be much doubt that someone has. Over the past few years, we've frequently been puzzled by the fact that what ought to have been rich lodes of ore running for a considerable distance have stopped short, contrary to the predictions of our geologists. And now, a matter of a month or two ago, we stumbled across this concealed mine gallery. And inside we found . . ."

He stepped for a moment into the low opening, having to stoop to avoid the roof, fumbled on the ground and turned back to Don Miguel, holding out something on his palm. Don Miguel took it, stared at it, and felt the world tremble around him.

THREE

His Highness the Prince of New Castile, Commander of the Society of Time, ran his fingers through his short black beard. He stared for a long while at the object on the table in front of him, and at last spoke.

"Well, since you seem to have a gift for turning up uncomfortable odds and ends, Navarro, I suppose I'll have to inquire what you make of this—this bit of scrap metal. I know you take it seriously enough to have abandoned your furlough in California, but I must say it seems to me an innocuous enough object . . . All right: why the song and dance?"

Don Miguel drew a deep breath and held it for the space of three heartbeats. He didn't need anyone to tell him he was going out on a limb; he would have been far happier if he had been able to consult with one of the Society's theoreticians—ideally, with Father Ramón himself—before making his suspicions public. But Father Ramón was on the other side of the Atlantic Ocean, and the Commander was here in New Madrid. And the discovery which Two Dogs had made was already two months in the past . . .

He licked his lips, very conscious of the piercing eyes of the many notables assembled in this, the Prince's audience chamber, and above all of the stare of the other Licentiates who were present. On his brief stopover at New Madrid *en route* to California he had made the unpleasant discovery that the members of the Society based here tended to resent his being awarded the Order of the Scythe and Hourglass at such an early age and attributed it not to anything he had done to merit the honour but to undue influence at the Headquarters Office of the Society in Londres.

If this gamble of his were to prove unwarranted . . .

But he shut away that possibility from his mind. Far too much was at stake for him to consider the risk of later personal disadvantage. And, anyway, was it not worse to be a prince than a commoner in so many ways? Imagine living in the public eye twenty-four hours a day, so that one could not rise from bed, conduct one's toilet, eat a meal, without scores of hangers-on in attendance! One could barely even enjoy a love-affair, come to that, without the crudest details filtering down in garbled form to the palace kitcheners!

Accordingly he set his shoulders back, looked his Commander straight in the eye, and spoke out boldly.

"What I make of it, sir, is this—though I'm open to correction. I think it's a breach of the Treaty of Prague."

Well . . . there was the bombshell. And it certainly went off to great effect. The Prince himself blanched and jerked back in his chair, while everyone else without exception paled and voiced wordless exclamations.

"By whom?" the Prince demanded sternly.

"By the other party to the Treaty—I assume. Either that, or else we have here the first recorded case of temporal interference by a time-traveller from some place not bound by treaty obligations."

There was a terrible silence in the audience chamber.

"You realise," the Prince said at length, "that this is the most serious allegation you could possibly make?"

Would I did not! But Don Miguel kept that thought to himself, and merely nodded.

"You have grounds?"

"I believe so, sir. Having conducted such on-the-spot investigations as were possible to me without time apparatus, I could come to no other conclusion."

The Prince put out one hairy-backed hand towards the harmless-looking chip of metal on the table before him. At the last moment before completing the gesture, he drew back as though from a sleeping snake. He said, "Clear the hall! At once! And if anyone breathes a word of this I'll have his head off his shoulders before nightfall—is that clear? Executioner! I know there are at least three incurable gossips whose tongues rattle day and night like dry peas in a bladder—have three stakes ready by this afternoon to mount their heads on!"

The man who stood by the door, black-masked and anonymous, bowed to acknowledge the order, and not a few of the courtiers shivered.

"Now get out!" barked the Prince. "All of you except Don Miguel, and make it fast!"

The Treaty of Prague, Don Miguel had often thought, was the most fragile bulwark ever interposed between man and the forces of primal chaos. It was like a plug of wet paper in the mouth of a volcano—yet it was the best they could contrive.

At the first moment when Don Carlos Borromeo discovered how time might be converted into a direction like other directions so that men might make voyages along it, he—whom some called very wise, others incurably bitter and disillusioned—had clearly foreseen the uses to which selfish and greedy men might put this miracle. Allegedly he had considered trying to suppress the knowledge altogether, but in the end, after consultation with his confessor, he had been compelled to accept that someone else might stumble on the same principle who was less sceptical about the ability of mankind to cope with powers beyond their previous dreams.

But, looking at the contemporary world around him, he had been faced with those intransigents who wished to reconquer Spain, the old heartland from which Christian civilisation had been driven by its virile Islamic rival, and who would not have been above sending back an army to ensure that alteration of history. Similarly there were those in the fretful, unstable Confederacy of the East who resented being part of a heterogeneous political alliance, and who would rather have seen Lithuania, or Poland, or Prussia, or even Russ, become an unquestionably dominant national power free from the need to consider the wishes of competing local interests.

Putting time-travel into the hands of men with such a background would be like smoking a tobacco-pipe in a powder-factory.

The best that could be hoped for, he decided, was that the technique of time-travel should be administered by men with proper scruples, aware of the responsibility their knowledge imposed on them and bound by oaths to obey the instructions of the wisest and most far-seeing officers who could be found to lead them.

Accordingly, having appealed to the Pope for a commission that empowered him to dictate to princes, kings and emperors under pain of instant excommunication, he set up the Society of Time and pledged its founding members to employ time-travel solely for the benefit of mankind, to increase the sum of human knowledge and not to interfere with the past.

Nonetheless, what he was afraid of happened: almost at once a party of lunatics began to agitate for the re-conquest of Spain. For a while it looked as though madness would overcome sense. Then, however, the balance was tipped back in favour of rationality. The Confederacy let it be known—discreetly, delicately—that they too had gained the secret of travelling in time. If an Imperial army went back to oppose the Moorish invasion of Spain, it would be met by corresponding forces determined to keep the *status quo*—for the Confederacy regarded the Empire as quite strong enough already without the retrospective addition of the Iberian peninsula to its territory.

It was whispered, but never proved, that Borromeo himself had given his secret to the Confederacy. At any rate, it was for the best; the Empire came to its senses, proposed Papal arbitration, and with the assistance of the Vatican's finest legal experts drafted the agreement which was ultimately signed in 1897 in the handsome and ancient city of Prague. The Treaty was Borromeo's last legacy. Three weeks after it was signed he died of a chill caught in the mists of Poland, for it was a bitter winter that year.

Perhaps, thought Don Miguel, he had died content. But it seemed unlikely. He must have suspected that sooner or later the Treaty by itself would prove inadequate, even though it plugged the dyke for a little while. He might not have foreseen that greed would so rapidly corrupt the very Licentiates who were supposed to be chosen for their honesty and integrity—yet Don Miguel knew, better than any of his colleagues bar Father Ramón, how near simple greed had already come to oversetting the fabric of history. Over and above that, though, there was the even more significant point that Borromeo must have been aware of: time apparatus was intrinsically so simple that eventually other scientists whose governments were not signatories to the Treaty would chance on the principle involved . . . or be sold the information by someone venal, someone with a grudge, someone mentally unstable.

Was the discovery which Two Dogs had made the first evidence in the twentieth century that some other power was due to develop time-travel? Would it prove to be an expedition from the Mediterranean Caliphate that was involved, or—more likely, considering the geographical location—temporal explorers from the Middle Kingdom of Cathay? Or intruders from Çipangu, those islands off the eastern coast of Asia whose people so greatly admired the Empire and who sought to turn their geographically analogous location into a politically analogous independence from the mainland culture of Cathay which had dominated virtually their entire recorded history?

Don Miguel doubted these latter possibilites. He was a great believer in the principle enunciated by William of Occam, the "razor" which advised one not to multiply assumptions more than necessary. And here one did not have to assume.

One merely had to deduce...

"It's good steel," he said, pointing to the object on the table between himself and the Prince. "It's the bit of a rock-drill, cracked in half. I've established beyond doubt that *we've* never mined that valley. And history shows us no one who knew how to make good steel and who passed through that part of California prior to our discovery of the New World. In company with Two Dogs, the mine manager, I searched the locality for several miles around. We discovered the traces of at least nine mine galleries, all bar the first caved in. Two Dogs has extensive grounding in mineralogy; he was able to estimate that these mines were worked approximately a thousand years ago. I spoke to several of his foremen and overseers, and they took me to see abandoned galleries of their own where what should have been extensive veins of ore had turned out to stop short instead of continuing for the predicted distances. It was that which finally drove me to the inescapable conclusion that we're here faced with an illegal intrusion into the past."

The Prince gave a slow nod of comprehension, his face bleaker than winter in Norroway. He said, "By whom and for what purpose, Navarro? What's your view?"

"Sir, I can only interpret what I've seen for myself." Don Miguel licked his lips. "I read the situation like this. It's notorious that these hills are among the richest mineral deposits in the world. I think the intruders decided to exploit them—perhaps for some metal, such as silver, which is essential to time-travel. In the present this was impossible, since we're already at work there, but in the past, of course, the area was empty bar a few naked Indians with no interest in mining. Perhaps they were, or are, not very experienced in geology, and took it for granted that when they had finished their work it would suffice to rely on natural causes to wipe away the traces of what they'd done. After all, California is earthquake country, and in a thousand years you'd expect mine galleries to cave in of their own accord. It must have been sheer chance that preserved the one in which Two Dogs discovered the drill-bit."

"So this thing"—the Prince picked up the scrap of steel—"has been lying in the ground for a thousand years! Yet it's barely marked with rust, isn't it?"

"As I said, sir, the mouth of the cave—of the mine gallery, rather—was closed by this balanced boulder. Earth and grass-roots had made an almost perfect seal around it, and the interior of the cave was dry. In any case the climate there is equable."

For some moments the Prince was silent. His dark eyes searched Don Miguel's face. At length he said heavily, "I wish it were not so, Navarro, but in my judgement you've made out a case. We'll get time apparatus to California as quickly as we can, and see if we can secure objective evidence." He rose to his feet. "Meantime, we'll also notify Londres, and bring out our most highly trained investigators. I'm not questioning your analysis of the situation, but you must appreciate that an unfounded charge concerning a breach of the Treaty of Prague could ruin the precarious trust we've managed to nurture between ourselves and the Temporal College."

"Sir," Don Miguel said with feeling. "I pray that I *am* wrong! For how much more disastrous it will be if I'm right!"

FOUR

Before the discovery of humane drugs to unlock the gates of truth in the human mind, there had been a torture—used even by the Holy Office—consisting in the placing upon the subject of a large wooden board, and in turn upon the board a succession of stones of increasing weight, so that in the end a stubborn man would be crushed like an insect beneath a boot.

For Don Miguel the next several weeks were like a session of such torture. And he was not the only one to suffer.

The first of the stones was a light one, and added nothing more to his burden of anxiety than simple confirmation of what he had already suspected. It had been rumoured for some while that more gold and silver were circulating in the Confederacy than their known resources could account for. The logical deduction was that new and so far secret lodes had been located, perhaps in the inhospitable unexplored wastes of Siberia.

Present information made it seem likelier that for "Siberia" should be substituted "California" . . .

The second stone was heavier and more painful. A metallurgical expert compared the mysterious drill-bit with samples of other steels, and reported unequivocally: made in Augsburg! It was of a type commonly used in the Confederacy, but hardly ever encountered elsewhere—certainly not in California, where a number of the trace constituents, notably cobalt, were unavailable.

The third, and heaviest, was a report from a team of men whom Two Dogs—at Don Miguel's urgent request—had set to searching the route between the site of the poachers' mine and the nearest convenient harbour on the coast. One of the earliest questions to have arisen, naturally, had been this: how did the poachers reach the site where their traces had been discovered? It was of course possible to operate a time apparatus to transmit its occupant spatially as well as temporally—all that was required was an adjustment of the dimensional relationships dictated by the power-carrying bars in its frame. So long as the gravitational potential at the arrival point was roughly the same as that at base, no harm would come to the traveller . . . although transmitting from a hilltop to a valley resulted in the messy dispersal of surplus potential energy and the death or injury of the victim.

Yet it seemed improbable that one should voyage blind across a thousand years and also displace oneself by several thousand miles; it would be a fearful leap into the dark, and there was the risk of the shape of the landscape having been changed by erosion or earthquake, so that one might arrive inside a hill, or in mid-air. It seemed more likely that the poachers must first have gone back in time at some place whose topography they could establish beyond doubt, and then at least a scouting party would have proceeded to the mining site by more conventional means.

And the men dispatched by Two Dogs, following the most obvious route to the sea, came across a ship's timber buried in the sand, of a form not commonly employed by the aboriginal inhabitants and in a condition to suggest it had been lying where they found it for some such period as a thousand years . . .

Driven almost to a frenzy by the cumulative pressure of this news, the experts sent out from New Madrid and Londres by the Society of Time redoubled the pace of their preparations. Transportable time apparatus was brought to the lonely Californian valley under habitual conditions of secrecy—few people outside the Society ever saw an actual time apparatus, because it was so dangerously simple, being composed only of bars of silver and magnetised iron in precisely determined relationships. It might have entered someone's head to make a model of what he had seen, with the disturbing consequence that the model might *work*.

Accordingly, a small town of canvas marquees bloomed in the sunlight, and the labourers and their families went by incuriously for the most part, occasionally pausing to watch, but not often, as yet one more manifestation of the madness of these Europeans intruded into their quiet private world.

On the evening of the day when suspicion turned to cruel certainty, Don Miguel encountered his friend Two Dogs again. Head bowed, he was plodding up the slope of the hill that separated the modern mining area from the one established by the poachers and feeling as though the limping world were using him for a crutch, when he heard his name called. Raising his eyes, he saw the Mohawk waiting on the path ahead, face inscrutable, prepared for any news.

"Well?" he said as Don Miguel approached.

"We found them," Don Miguel said. "At the summer of A.D. 984. They killed a Mohawk Licentiate who showed himself to them. And they used a gun."

Two Dogs gave a slow nod. He said, "So your millstones are going to grind again, and this time we shall be ground between them."

"What do you mean?" Don Miguel said. But he was too weary to be genuinely interested in the reply.

"I should have thought it was obvious. Did you not imply that you've found what you expected—poachers from the Confederacy?"

"Yes, there isn't any doubt. They were seen, as I said. What's more, they were overheard talking."

"In that case, it follows that there's been a breach of the Treaty of Prague—am I not correct?"

"It would appear so. I'm not an expert, though, and we're waiting for Father Ramón himself now, who's supposed to be on the way from Londres, so I won't commit myself."

There was a pause. At last the Mohawk said musingly, "You are a strange people—you really are! When it came to matters of honour and justice, my ancestors didn't wait to consult some far-distant expert. We made our own minds up and acted in accordance with the principles we believed in, heedless of the consequences to ourselves. And I'd always been told that this was also the hidalgo code, the reason why it was the Spanish among all the competing European intruders who managed to form a successful alliance with the Red Indians rather than the French or the Swedes."

"True enough." In spite of his tiredness, Don Miguel felt a stir of interest provoked by the Mohawk's argument. Cultural analysis was inevitably a subject he'd had to delve into deeply before completing his training as a time-traveller.

"So why are you not acting to set right the injustice that's been done to you?"

"Because it's not only ourselves we must consider," Don Miguel pointed out. "This is a temporal matter. One ill-judged action might so deform history that we ruled ourselves out of existence—and you along with us."

"While admiring your scruples," Two Dogs murmured, "I still find your behaviour puzzling. I've been reading up on matters connected with time-travel recently, since this business broke out, and it seems to me that you could wipe out the poachers, couldn't you, at the end of their stay? I mean, when the changes their mining had wrought in the landscape corresponded to what can be seen in the present day."

"Oh, possibly! In fact, that may well be the course we have to adopt in the end. But . . ." Don Miguel shook his head unhappily. "We'd risk creating a closed causative loop, you see, where a future action entailed past consequences, and this is something so dangerous one dare not commit oneself before examining every alternative."

Although if the alternative is the death of a king . . .

But he firmly suppressed recollection of that New Year's night when he had had the truth of what he was now saying so fearfully demonstrated.

"If they're allowed to get away with it, though, surely these poachers will be tempted to repeat what they've done? Elsewhere, I mean. The next place you run across them may be in your coal-mines at home, or the Cornish tin-mines, or some other place where you can ill afford to lose what you have close to the heart of the Empire."

"But they won't be allowed to get away with it. A Papal

interdict will certainly follow concrete proof of their interference, and if necessary the whole Confederacy could be put
under ban."

"And this, you think, is a powerful enough weapon to
dissuade men who've already shown they're willing to tamper
with the past? If they're unafraid of material consequences
due to meddling with history, are they likely to be impressed
by the threat of spiritual displeasures from one old man
sitting on a throne in Rome?"

"You're a hard-bitten sceptic, aren't you?" Don Miguel
exclaimed. "Are you . . .? No, I'm sorry; it's not something
I'm entitled to ask."

"Ask what you like." Two Dogs shrugged. "By my
tradition, to call a man a friend is to make him a brother, and
a brother is permitted to know anything about you."

Don Miguel still hesitated. Eventually he said, "Well, I was
actually going to ask whether you're not a believer."

Two Dogs gave a wry chuckle. "You are, I take it?" he
countered, and without waiting for the foregone reply continued, "As a matter of fact, I am, but not a Catholic. Not
even what you would regard as a Christian, come to that. Oh,
I was raised as one—sent for the ordinary priestly education
of your European mission-schools—and I was taught a lot of
facts about the world which our own tradition ignored or
overlooked. But there were so many contradictions that
ultimately I was driven out of the fold by my conscience."

Don Miguel had vaguely heard that there was a revival of
pre-contact faiths currently developing among the Mohawks
—correction, echoing Two Dogs's own words many weeks
ago: among the Indians whom the Imperials casually sub-
sumed all under the one tribal name of "Mohawk." But this
was the first inkling he'd had that Two Dogs himself might

belong to this movement. He said, with great curiosity, "What were these—these contradictions?"

"Oh! I couldn't reconcile your commitment to a Prince of Peace with what you did in the way of massacring my ancestors—nor could I reconcile your ability to travel in time with your unwillingness to go back and see for yourselves the true nature of the Saviour you worship."

That had, more than once, troubled Don Miguel also. He said with feigned certainty, this time hearing Father Ramón in his memory, "But we have visited the time of Jesus's ministry. A new Pope, for instance, is always permitted to hear Christ speak following his accession, and over nearly a hundred years the Church has survived any consequences. Whatever you may think of Christ as a Son of God, surely it follows that He was a very exceptional man."

"Perhaps. But exceptional in his day and his environment. I've been told that my great-great grandfather was the most skilful buffalo-hunter his tribe had ever seen. Fine! Marvellous! But since you brought guns to this country, who can live by killing buffalo? Admire him, I may—but am I to imitate him now that the buffalo are rare to the point where they have to be protected?"

Don Miguel found he had no immediate answer to that. He shrugged and wiped his face, and at once Two Dogs was contrite. Stepping forward and putting a hand around his friend's shoulders, he said, "But I'm being cruel, keeping you out in the hot sun arguing about abstracts! Here, we'll go and sit on my verandah for a while and drink a few glasses of our local wine that you seem to enjoy so much, and talk about things which don't involve the fate of the universe."

Don Miguel gave a wan smile. "That," he said feelingly, "would be a very welcome relief."

FIVE

Don Arturo Cortés came to the isolated valley, who still had the look of a man haunted by the ghost of himself, and who had not been a friend of Don Miguel's until he saw that ghost; Don Felipe Basso came, and said that the Lady Kristina was sad at not having seen Don Miguel again but had had to leave Londres suddenly upon her father being appointed Ambassador to the Confederacy of the East; Father Ramón came, and unlike the other two showed no sign of strain from his appalling journey, night and day from New Madrid in the huge cushion-wheeled transcontinental express-wagon which stopped only to change horses and pick up provisions.

Don Miguel saw the last relay of horses as they were led away from the wagon. They looked ready for the knacker.

These three, the night of their arrival, forgathered with Don Miguel and the two experts from New Madrid who had taken temporary charge of the investigation until their seniors from Londres could reach the spot; of these, one was an Inquisitor. They met in one of the huge marquees set up by the Society's technicians just over the hill from the mines which Two Dogs managed. There was a breeze at nightfall, and their shadows—cast by flaring lamps on to the white canvas—moved in eerie fashion as they sat around their table.

Don Rodrigo Juarez had personally conducted the expedition to the year 984 on which the existence of the poachers had been proved. Though he had been born and bred in New Castile rather than Europe, his reputation stood high, and since what had happened last New Year to Don Arturo Cortés men had begun to speak of him, rather than Don Arturo, as Red Bear's probable successor in the key post of Director of Fieldwork. Don Rodrigo was aware of what was being said, and moreover was pleased to find that Don Arturo did too; this—to Don Miguel's way of thinking—endowed his manner with an unpleasant smugness almost as nasty as Don Arturo's former overweening arrogance.

But there was no time now for personal likes and dislikes. There was the very structure of history to be underpinned.

"What we found," said Don Rodrigo, "left absolutely no room for doubt. We saw the poachers at work, and we heard them talking among themselves. To avoid anachronism we were clothed—*unclothed*, rather, ha-ha!—like Indians such as we know frequented California in those days. I called for a volunteer to show himself at their encampment, and a Mohawk Licentiate from New Castile, named Roan Horse, came forward. Without questioning him, they shot him dead. I agree with Don Miguel Navarro: we have a crime far greater than mere murder, foul though that may be. We have indubitably a breach of the Treaty of Prague!"

He sat back, jutting out his jaw. He was a large man whose

mother had been Scots, and his gingery hair and lantern chin stemmed from her family.

All eyes turned to Father Ramón, who had been listening with total concentration to Don Rodrigo's views. Keenest of all to hear the Jesuit's opinion was Don Miguel; his mind was aching almost physically.

"Not proven," said Father Ramón at length.

"What?" All of them said it, except Don Felipe, who was keeping himself to himself in such distinguished company.

"Not proven!" Father Ramón turned his bird-like head to regard them one after the other. "For various reasons. Not the least compelling grounds for witholding judgement can be found here: a breach of the Treaty is of its nature an irremediable disaster to be avoided at all costs. Luckily one has not yet been committed."

"But—!" Don Rodrigo expostulated. Father Ramón's thin hand went up to interrupt him.

"No, hear me out, if you please. Before leaving Londres I checked your qualifications. They're admirable. But they omit one important item. You've never attended the School of Casuistry in Rome; if you had, you'd have gone through a gruelling course of disputation on this very subject of a breach of the Treaty of Prague. Believe me, when the Vatican's experts framed that Treaty, they did not do so in a hurry, or in such a way as to leave loopholes."

"I'm not talking about sneaking through a loophole!" flared Don Rodrigo. "I'm talking about poachers who've torn it up and spat on the shreds!"

Calmly Father Ramón stared him down. "You should know better that that," he said at length. "In your position you should. Don Miguel's reaction is forgivable; in the ordinary course of his career he would not be due to attend the School of Casuistry for another five years or so. Your colleague, however, I'm also surprised at." He bent a frown on the Inquisitor. "How say you, Brother Vasco?"

The man shifted on his hard bench. He said, "I'm reserving my judgement until I can consult a text I needn't name. There's no copy nearer than New Madrid, and I confess my memory of it has worn thin."

The Jesuit pursed his lips. After a moment he shrugged. "Well, there's no need to prolong the argument, is there? Don Arturo, if I recall correctly, *has* attended the School, and should by now be bursting with the right solution."

They looked at Don Arturo, their heads moving as though pulled by strings, and saw him pass his hand shakily across his face. "Solutions to the present problem I have none, Father," he said. "But I know one thing almost beyond doubt."

"Which is . . .?" prompted Father Ramón.

"There hasn't been a breach of the Treaty of Prague because such a thing is virtually inconceivable."

Don Miguel glanced at his friend Don Felipe, and received in return a look which said, "I'm out of my depth here." He turned back to the Jesuit.

"I—I seem to have been over-hasty," he began, and got no further. Smiling, and looking as usual when he did so like a parchment-covered skull, Father Ramón shook his head.

"Save your apologies, my son. They're not justified. An intent to break the Treaty is perfectly conceivable, and it appears that this is what you've chanced upon. Let me clarify the situation in the terms which I think the judge of a Papal court would use." He raised one bony finger.

"*Imprimis*: the death of Roan Horse. He was an extemporate, was he not? His death in the past was due to causes

whose prime origin lay in the present, because he was shot by
another extemporate, and the effects began to be manifest at
a moment in present time which was demonstrably later than
the moment of his departure. It may also be later than the
point from which the—the *poachers*, as you graphically term
them, departed to the past. This is not certain, but the
evidence we now have indicates it."

"But Roan Horse was one of my best men!" Don Rodrigo
burst out. "And they shot him down, in cold blood!"

"There are penalties for murder," said Father Ramón. "It
is not, however, a crime with which the Treaty of Prague is
concerned, and that is what we're presently discussing."
Another finger went up.

"*Secundo*: there is a particular clause in the Treaty under
which you, Don Rodrigo, are no doubt champing to frame an
indictment. It states, in sum, that neither signatory to the
agreement will act in such a way in past times as to cause a
disadvantage to the other party discernible in present time. It
makes no reference to hypothetical future disadvantage and
since mining operations have not even yet spread from this
valley to the adjacent one where the poachers dug their shafts
it is only future disadvantage that's in question."

"Ridiculous!" fumed Don Rodrigo. "All right, they took
their ore from shafts dug in the next valley, not in the one
we're at present mining—nonetheless, the mine manager says
his men have frequently found that veins of ore stopped
before they should have done, causing them to go back and
dig fresh galleries when they ought to have been able to
extend the existing ones for a long way yet. If that isn't
'disadvantage,' I don't know what is!" He leaned back and
concluded with bad grace, "Much as it pains me to contradict
an expert of your calibre, I feel you're overlooking some-

thing."

"Nothing," the Jesuit murmured. "Or rather, not I but the experts in disputation who have spent the better part of a century thrashing out possible interpretations of the Treaty." He lifted a third finger. "I say further that *tertio* disadvantage discernible in present time was not caused to us because it was not at the present time of discovery of these veins of ore that Don Miguel Navarro interpreted the facts to indicate previous interference."

Even Don Felipe gaped at the appalling casuistry of that remark. As for Don Miguel, he could not restrain himself from an explosive—but fortunately wordless—reaction. Father Ramón turned to him.

"I know what you're thinking, my son," he said. "You're wondering why, if this is so, we should not ourselves systematically go and rifle the prehistoric ages of the territory now occupied by the Confederacy, so as to render their lands poor and barren. I can answer that immediately. It wasn't done. And why should it be done? What profit is there in it? If we did it to them, they'd do it to us, and each would wind up with the other's resources at the cost of infinitely greater effort."

He switched his penetrating gaze back to Don Rodrigo. "What you've either forgotten or never realised, my son, is that the Treaty of Prague is unique. Alone among the agreements and covenants made between men or nations throughout history, the punishment for breaking it is laid down not by the men who drafted it, but by God who created the universe. And for that reason it is worse than foolish to expend your efforts on showing that a breach of it has been committed. It is very nearly sinful. Putting it bluntly: the Treaty of Prague can be broken, but—must—not!"

He marked each word of the last phrase with a tap of his

bony fist on the table, and in rhythm with the sounds the colour in Don Rodrigo's cheeks heightened until it was vivid as a sunset. Seeing him blush, Don Arturo smiled for the first time that Don Miguel could remember since the terrible New Year's Eve of the current year.

To save himself from having to dwell on his private recollections of that dreadful night, Don Miguel said aloud, "But some action must be taken, nonetheless!"

"Indubitably," the Jesuit agreed. "May we hear your own proposals concerning it?"

Don Miguel stumbletongued. He said, "Why—why, I have no definite plan. Indeed, I've been wondering whether our action may not be fore-ordained! Two Dogs suggested that we should step in and drive away the poachers at the point where their work had resulted in exactly the traces which he and his men discovered, and reflecting on the idea I began to suspect that a closed causative loop must exist which gives rise to precisely those traces we've found in the present."

"This is highly probable," agreed Father Ramón. "Evidently something prevented the poachers from exhausting the entire mineral resources of the area, and the likeliest explanation is that they were interrupted and compelled to abandon their work."

"In that case," Don Rodrigo said, "our course of action is plain. We must at once send back an armed party to effect this—this compulsory abandonment of their mines."

"Not at all," Father Ramón countered. "We must go back, certainly—but to speak with them, learn who they are, and instruct them to depart."

"Speak with them?" Don Rodrigo echoed scornfully. "But they shot down Roan Horse on his mere appearance!"

"I doubt if they will fire on an obvious extemporate.

Especially if he wears the cloth."

That took a moment to sink in. Brother Vasco was the first to react. "Father, you're not thinking of going alone!" he exclaimed.

"No, indeed. By way of imprinting a little lesson on a certain party who has—not for the first time—acted too impulsively, I shall go in the company of . . . Don Miguel Navarro."

He did not switch his gaze to Don Miguel until he had finished speaking. The latter, not much relishing the prospect of facing the poachers under these circumstances, but resigned to the idea since it came from Father Ramón, gave a shrug.

"As you say, Father. It appears that I've started a panic which isn't justified by the legalities of the matter."

"Good." Father Ramón glanced at his watch, and stood up. "It's late, and after my journey I'm somewhat weary. Tomorrow I'll require the use of your time apparatus, and we'll settle the problem—God willing—once for all."

"What's been decided, Don Miguel?" came the soft question from Two Dogs. He was sitting out late on his verandah; on the floor at his feet Conchita, his serving-maid and mistress, was picking ethereal chords from her cuatro, a small four-stringed guitar. He had offered her to Don Miguel a couple of times when first the latter came to stay here, but that was so far from the customs of home he had refused automatically, and the offer had not been repeated. Subsequently he had looked again at Conchita, who was slim, berry-brown and graceful as a dancer, and regretted the fact. He would have welcomed the mere physical relief of her company as a key to the sleep which worry had so often denied him these past several weeks.

He sat down wearily in the guest-chair, and waited while Two Dogs dismissed Conchita with a gesture; she went like a shadow, silently. Then he said, "There's been no breach of the Treaty."

For a long moment Two Dogs did not comment. Finally he said in a tight, controlled voice, "How's that possible? Surely they don't doubt there's been interference with the past!"

"You're too practical a man to follow the casuistry of it." Don Miguel shut his eyes and rubbed at them to relieve their tiredness. "I can barely make it out myself. But what it comes down to is that instead of going back and driving the poachers away, we're simply going to pay them a—a sort of social call. Father Ramón and myself. What good that will do, Lord knows."

Two Dogs laughed harshly. He said, "Indeed you Europeans are strange beyond comprehension. There's no consistency in your behaviour! You travelled half a world from home, risked your lives, drove away my ancestors from their hunting-grounds for the sake of gold and silver—and now, when someone is filching away what you spilled so much blood to secure, you say you're going to have a little chat with the thieves!"

Don Miguel was too fatigued to frame a reply. There was a short silence. At length Two Dogs rose to his feet.

"Well, I suppose it's a small consolation that your mill-stones won't be grinding us after all. I'll bid you good night, then, and wish you sharp wits in your discussion with the poachers. Though if it were up to me I'd counsel more substantial weapons."

SIX

As Don Miguel had expected, the valley had changed so little in a thousand years that it was not incongruous to find a mining encampment when they walked over the brow of the hill behind which, to escape immediate observation, they had chosen to arrive. There had no doubt been earth movements; there were subtle differences in the outlines of some of the nearby slopes. But the identity of the landscape at the two time-points was unmistakable.

He felt a stir of admiration for the magnificently simple stage-management of Father Ramón's plan. When they emerged on the crest of the hill and let the poachers see them, the impact was instantaneous. Watchful guards raised guns to their shoulders—checked—and let the muzzles slowly fall again, within the space of a dozen heartbeats. Indians such as were to be expected at this moment of time would no doubt have been fired on to drive them away, as had happened to

Roan Horse. But the sight of Father Ramon in his sombre habit and Don Miguel wearing—at the Jesuit's insistence—the jewelled collar and star of the Order of the Scythe and Hourglass conspicuously glittering on his plain shirt: this was a message to inform the poachers without words that their presence and their plans were known.

They waited, a light breeze touching their faces, while news of their arrival spread. Don Miguel had his first chance to study the tented settlement, the mouths of the galleries, the sluices and sedimentation troughs and all the rest of the equipment, so like the mine which Two Dogs managed that he had to keep forcibly reminding himself he was more than a thousand years from home.

Work stopped. Harsh barking orders brought men out of the mine galleries to blink in the sunlight. Overseers—not a few of whom, Don Miguel was dismayed to see, wore the uniform of the Temporal College—snapped at each other and their subordinates.

Still the newcomers waited on the crest of the hill, for fully five minutes in the baking sun of late summer, until at last a big, burly man detached himself from the ant-milling crowd and came to meet them, accompanied by two of the uniformed overseers.

"Good day, sirs," he said in heavily accented Spanish. "I do not have to inquire the reason for your presence. Permit me to present myself: the Margrave Friedrich von Feuerstein, High Brother of the Temporal College and Deputy Master of the Wenceslas Brigade. I presume your honour to be Father Ramón of the Society of Time?"

The Jesuit inclined his head. "We've met before. Though it seems you've forgotten the fact. In Rome, at the School of Casuistry. My class was departing as yours arrived."

"Indeed, of course!" the Margrave exclaimed, and extended his hand. "Strange that our acquaintance should be renewed here and now!"

Father Ramón ignored the proffered hand. He said, "No it's far from strange. Are you in charge of this—this *venture*?"

The Margrave folded his arms across his chest and drew back a pace, scowling. He said, "Yes, I'm in charge. Why?"

Father Ramón reached inside his habit and produced a rolled parchment. With his bird-claw fingers he undid the fastening and shook it out; from its bottom a heavy red seal swung on a ribbon. He seemed suddenly to speak in a voice other than his own, holding the scroll up as though to read from it but looking all the time at the Margrave.

"This," he said, "is a copy of a Papal bull. Do I have to tell you that it is the bull *De tenebris temporalibus*?"

The Margrave smiled. He was a large-jowled man with grey hair; the smile made plump hummocks of his cheeks, on the crest of each of which showed a red network of broken veins. He said, "I defy you to show cause for invoking that bull."

"I am not required to show cause." Father Ramón stared unblinkingly. "You have twelve hours, present time, in which to remove your men, your equipment and all traces of your presence here up to the point which we decree, on pain of summary excommunication by the powers vested in us under the aforesaid bull. I read!" He snapped the nail of a forefinger against the stiff parchment so that it sounded like a beaten drum, and still without looking away from the Margrave began to recite.

"*De tenebris temporalibus et de itineribus per tempus leges instituendae sunt. In nomine Deo Patri Filio et Spiritu Sancto dicimus et affirmamus . . .*"

The whole world seemed to hesitate to hear the rolling Latin syllables ring out through the hot still air. *Concerning the shades of time past and concerning journeys through time laws are to be instituted. In the name of God the Father, Son and Holy Ghost we say and affirm* . . . Don Miguel felt his lips move on the familiar words he had never before heard invoked.

"We say and affirm that the means of travelling in time is a gift bestowed by divine ordinance and therefore to be used only in accordance with divine law, subject to regulation by bodies of upright, just and sober men, to conditions now or in the future laid down by Papal decree, and to the expedient judgement of those agents now or in the future appointed by us for the enforcement of those conditions. Let there be agreements between nations and before God to employ the means of travelling in time for the benefit of humanity and the increase of human knowledge that we may the better comprehend and admire our Creator, and let there be penalties imposed upon those who for evil ends pervert and misuse this mystery."

The Margrave waited patiently until Father Ramón re-rolled the parchment with a crisp rustle, and then he said merely, "Tell me, Father—where is this 'evil' you're alleging?"

"A thousand years hence, and you're its victim, sir."

The words in themselves meant nothing to Don Miguel —and little enough, apparently, to the Margrave—but the tone in which they were uttered held a ring of indefinable menace, and he shivered. Noting his reaction, Father Ramón gave a faint smile.

"Be easy in your mind, my son," he murmured, "It will be clear in a little while." And to the Margrave he added, "Is there somewhere we can speak in confidence?"

"Yes! Yes, in my pavilion below. I'll see we're not disturbed or overheard." The Margrave made to turn, but lingered for a long moment trying to read the expression on the Jesuit's face. Failing, he led the way down the slope. The two overseers demanded what they should tell their men, and he instructed them curtly to halt work until given further orders. It was plain that they were puzzled by this, but glad of a rest, for the heat was scorching.

"Now explain yourself!" the Margrave said, letting fall the door-flap of his ornately striped and scalloped pavilion. It bore the arms of the Temporal College: a silver clockface on black, with the order of the figures running in reverse around the dial.

"It seems to me you have more to explain than I," Father Ramón countered.

The Margrave shook his head vigorously and plumped into a chair. "You've invoked the bull. I can choose to co-operate, or I can choose to resist. Persuade me."

"As you wish." Father Ramón set his sharp elbows on the table separating them. "To begin with, contrary to what I imagine you're thinking, we're not here to complain about your pilfering a few tons of ore from ground which is to become Imperial territory by treaty with the Mohawk Nation several centuries from now. Right now there's probably a sounder legal claim for freebooter's rights in the ore than for Mohawk rights. They were nowhere near this part of the world—I correct myself: they *are* nowhere near, and indeed I doubt they could be found to exist as a precedent tribal unit."

The Margrave was by this time unashamedly bewildered. He made to speak, but the Jesuit raised his hand.

"Hear me out! On the subject of the Mohawks, then: it's no

secret that they're the Empire's uneasiest allies. But this doesn't imply that they're automatically friends of yours, does it?''

The Margrave's face set into an impassive mask, and he sat up very straight in his chair. Don Miguel attempted to look as though he knew what Father Ramón was talking about, but he was as confused now as the Margrave had been a moment earlier. What had the Empire-Mohawk alliance to do with this shameless temporal poaching?

"Now it's true that you're perilously close to a breach of the Treaty of Prague. If it weren't deliberately framed to be unbreakable in all foreseeable circumstances, you'd have broken it already. We want to keep the Treaty intact."

"Doubletalk," the Margrave said curtly, and Don Miguel found himself inclined to agree.

"Are you determined to act in breach of the Treaty of Prague?" snapped Father Ramón.

"Of course not! As you just said, it's framed so as to be virtually unbreakable."

"But you think the Empire-Mohawk alliance is not," said Father Ramón.

There was a long, cold silence. Finally the Margrave rose to his feet. His voice had changed completely when he spoke again. It was heavier and somehow rang false, like a counterfeit coin.

"Very well. I'll clear the site and call the operation off."

Whatever had happened, it was effective, but Don Miguel still hadn't figured out why when he found himself charged by Father Ramón to supervise the removal from this day and age of all the equipment used by the poachers, an order grudgingly acceded to by the Margrave, who looked as though the sky had fallen on his head. The clerks provided fair copies of the equipment manifests so that Don Miguel could confirm they were taking back every item whose presence might linger through a thousand years, and he checked them off until his head was swimming: picks, drills, sieves, shovels, chisels, crowbars, saws, hatchets, axes, guns, shot, powderhorns . . .

The sluices and sedimentation troughs were chopped into fragments and piled on a vast bonfire, the tents were struck and rolled, the pit-props were hauled out from the mine galleries by teams of men tugging on ropes, and even the nails were torn loose and bagged for return to the twentieth century. Scowling, cursing, but compelled to obey, the poachers sweated at their tasks and at last, in the gathering dusk, faded back to where they had come from, leaving the valley once more as empty as it had been.

Except for Father Ramón and Don Miguel, who now at last had the chance to utter the question which had plagued him all day long.

"Father, what on earth did you do to convince the Margrave? I simply don't understand anything about this—neither what they were up to here, nor what you meant by your references to the Mohawk alliance, nor why they packed up and went home so tamely when there were two of us and over two hundred of them . . . !"

"I'm hardly surprised," Father Ramón said wryly. "I confess I hadn't expected to be shown so spectacularly right. I was more guessing than certain of the reason for this ridiculous adventure by the Confederacy."

The last of the poachers vanished into the gloom; there was the inevitable wash of heat, like the opening of a furnace door, which accompanied temporal displacements. Father Ramón waited like a statue for long seconds. Then he said,

"Have you means of making a light?"

"Yes."

"Come with me, then."

He started across the now deserted valley towards the mouth of the gallery which Two Dogs was to show to Don Miguel a thousand years hence. It was of course closed by the counterpoised boulder, but that was freshly placed, and the shifting of the earth which would later call for the strength of two men to make it roll had not yet occurred. Father Ramón set his shoulder to it and gave a gentle heave; before Don Miguel could come to his aid it had settled into the adjacent cup-shaped depression.

"Strike your light," the Jesuit said briskly.

Don Miguel complied, holding up the fizzing fusee at the full stretch of his arm.

"Now carry it into the gallery. Search carefully along the walls and floor right to the end."

Much puzzled, Don Miguel did so. He found nothing except various footmarks left by the workmen and the scars of their excavating tools. And, as he was coming back, he realised what Father Ramón was implying.

"It's not here!" he exclaimed, emerging into the open and tossing the burnt-out fusee away.

"You mean this?" Father Ramón felt in a pouch at his waist and produced the cracked drill-bit which Two Dogs had given to Don Miguel, the key to the whole affair. "No, I didn't think it would be. Before my departure from Londres I made some inquiries of—well, of certain trusted agents. I'm prepared to state that this drill-bit was purchased in Augsburg over the counter of an ordinary shop, the winter before last; I mean, naturally, in our own time. And it was purchased by a Mohawk."

He tossed it up and caught it again. Dim twilight glinted on the shiny broken edges. "Replace the stone, please, my son. I think we should go back and put a few questions to your affable acquaintance the mine manager—Two Dogs, isn't that his name? I think we'll discover he's not merely what he claims, but someone of far superior calibre and *very* much more dangerous."

Bending to replace the boulder, Don Miguel said explosively, "But I knew already! I had the equipment manifests in my hands, and I checked that the number of drill-bits returned to the present was the same as the total brought here!"

"Yes, I watched that phase of the operation with considerable attention. You have many admirable qualities, including the ability to see the grand pattern from a few clues and hints, but I can't say that attention to small details is your especial forte . . . is it?" But his eyes were twinkling as he uttered the formal reproof.

"Come now, hurry along. We've already had a long day here, and now we must go back and face another."

SEVEN

It was always the strangest quirk of time-travel that a man might go back a thousand years to a later time of day, and feel below the conscious level of his mind that he had travelled forward, while by returning from a late hour to an earlier one he would feel he had travelled back. It was dizzying, as usual, to emerge from the evening dusk of the year 984 to the high noon glare of 1989.

Several Licentiates of the Society were gathered to greet them, headed by Don Rodrigo, who—possibly to atone for his discourtesy towards Father Ramón last night—did not at once pester them with questions, but urged them to come sit in the shade of an awning and ordered wine and food to be brought.

That was very welcome. Having gulped down a long refreshing draught of wine chilled by standing in a mountain stream, Don Miguel felt prepared to cope with the world again. Rejecting Don Rodrigo's solicitous suggestion of a pipe of tobacco with a word of thanks, he glanced around to see who precisely had assembled to hear Father Ramón's report. Don Arturo was here, naturally, and so was Don Felipe; so too was the Inquisitor, Brother Vasco. But in addition, several—indeed, if memory served him, all—the Mohawk Licentiates present at the site had come together, and their faces were like stone masks.

Of course. Roan Horse was killed, and he was one of their company.

Don Miguel started as he realised that that episode had not even been mentioned during their confrontation with the Margrave.

That was something the Mohawks here would not enjoy being told.

"Well now, Father Ramón!" Don Rodrigo said importantly. "What news have you brought?"

"The affair is dealt with," the Jesuit said. "The poachers have ceased operations and the matter is closed."

There was silence. Everyone was expecting him to say something more, even Don Miguel. When at length it became clear he had no intention of doing so, Don Rodrigo said feebly, "But—"

"But nothing, my son. I told you: the matter is closed."

The people around exchanged startled glances. On the fringe of the group Don Miguel saw one of the Mohawk Licentiates whisper to a friend, and then slip away. For a moment he let his gaze follow; then an outburst from Brother Vasco drew back his attention.

"But—Father! You haven't even told us who they were!"

"A group of misguided adventurers from the Confederacy. Unmasked, they went home like whipped curs, their tails

between their legs, and will certainly not trouble us again."
Don Miguel could detect that Father Ramón was forcing
himself to be patient, but equally sympathised with the
listeners who wanted more positive information.

The same Mohawk whose friend had whispered to him just
now shouldered through the group of Licentiates and con-
fronted Father Ramón. "That's not good enough!" he barked.
"What about the death of Roan Horse?"

"The identity of the man responsible is known. We shall
demand full recompense from the Confederacy."

A buzz of comment was going around now, like the droning
of flies in the hot sunlight. The Mohawk spoke again.

"That's disgraceful! What compensation is adequate for
the life of a good friend and a brave man?"

There was a chorus of agreement. Don Felipe put in, "And
surely, Father, the fact stands: taking the ore they stole is
temporal contrabandage!"

"To the infernal fires with your gold and silver!" the
Mohawk cried. "We're concerned with the fate of a man who
was brutally shot down!"

It was then that facts clicked together in Don Miguel's
mind. The only excuse he could offer himself for having
overlooked the obvious twice in one day was that he was
confused by tiredness.

"Felipe!" he snapped, bounding to his feet, and Don Felipe
Basso whirled to face him. "Sword—quickly! And with me
over the hill!"

He shoved his way unceremoniously through the circle of
Licentiates, and Felipe—not knowing why, but impressed by
his friend's urgency—came after him.

"Wait, you!" the Mohawk snapped, and strode to block
Don Miguel's way. "We want to hear from you about all this,

as well as Father Ramón!"

Almost, Don Miguel unsheathed his sword, but as yet he had only suspicion to go on. Instead he placed one palm flat on the Mohawk's chest and hooked a toe behind his ankle, sending him sprawling. The sudden commotion had bewildered everyone, but he saw that Don Arturo appeared to have kept his head, and barked at him.

"Hold this man—call for help and detain his companions! Stop 'em chasing us over the hill! One of them has slipped away, though, and we may already be too late!"

Not waiting to see how well the instruction was obeyed, he gestured to Don Felipe and began to run up the hillside track towards the home of Two Dogs. Behind him there was a shouting and a stamping of feet, but he dared not glance behind for fear of losing his footing on the rough pathway.

Breasting the rise after a short eternity, he found he was indeed too late.

Alongside the mud-plastered house where he had spent so many nights as a guest, he saw Tomás standing inscrutable in his colourful *serape*. He was shading his eyes to look towards a cloud of dust on the road that led to the sea—and in that cloud of dust could be discerned two horses, not the stumbling burros of the locality, but horses of the finest racing stock, being ridden as though to outpace the devil himself.

"Miguel!" panted Don Felipe, drawing abreast of his friend. "What's all the fuss about?"

"The birds have flown—and there's the whole continent and ocean for them to hide in!" Don Miguel pointed. "Go call some men together, give them the best horses we have, and send them in pursuit. One of those fugitives is Two Dogs, and he's probably the most dangerous man in the world!"

Don Felipe threw up his hands in hopeless bewilderment,

but turned back. Instantly he uttered a wordless exclamation, and Don Miguel also swung round. With a sinking heart he saw that down in the other valley there was a flashing of steel, and some of it was smeared with red. Red, too, was spreading across the dark habit of the bird-like figure seated in the shade of the awning.

"Father Ramón!" Don Miguel cried, drawing his sword. Together with Don Felipe he launched himself back down the slope.

"He told me himself!" Don Miguel mourned as he set aside the leather water-bottle from which he had slaked his dreadful thirst. "He told me in plain words, and fool that I am I didn't understand!"

"Told you what?" Don Arturo demanded eagerly. He and all the other non-Mohawk Licentiates were hanging on Don Miguel as though his words were pearls of perfect wisdom. They were leaning on him as they had been used to lean on Father Ramón.

But Father Ramón was dead. And he was not the only one.

If they knew how little I've actually learned, how much is simply a guess . . .

Don Miguel dared not speak that thought, though. For better or worse, he was the man on whom this crisis turned.

Wearily he said, "He told me that calling him a Mohawk was like calling me a Spaniard. There's Spanish blood in my veins all right, I speak Spanish and bear a Spanish name, but I'm not a Spaniard. I'm a citizen of the Empire, and I may well never set foot in Spain before I die. So too with a Mohawk like Two Dogs; an accident of history makes us call him by the name of a tribe whose hunting-grounds are three thousand miles away, and in his veins there's more blood from other tribes, equally proud, mortally resentful that thanks to us intruders from Europe their nationhood, their identity, has been effaced. We say *Mohawk* because it was our alliance with the Mohawk Nation which enabled that tribe to become the dominant power on the continent, subjugating the Crees and the Cherokees and the Apaches and the Sioux . . . Oh, scores of them, scores of separate peoples! But it wasn't their intrinsic superiority which brought about their supremacy. It was the guns we gave them, the Arab horses that could out-gallop the little ponies the other tribes owned, the wagons that carried their armoury of powder and shot on the trails to the west! Suppose we'd become the major power in Europe thanks not to our own skills and persistence, but to being patronised by the Moors—would you expect the French and English and Dutch to have any love for us, hey?"

He glared fiercely around the circle of his audience to see if they understood what he was telling them.

Don Rodrigo, his left arm in a sling thanks to a wild slash by one of the Mohawk Licentiates they had had to put under arrest, uttered a doubtful grunt. "You say they hate us because they're not all genuinely Mohawk by extraction. But I've worked for years with—with *native* Licentiates at New Madrid. Certainly some of them were Mohican rather than Mohawk, and others were Oneida and Seneca and Algonquin. But it never seemed to make any difference; we all got along very well."

"These Indians are proud people," Don Miguel said with a sigh. "They do not show that they are humiliated—it goes against their code. But they remember that they're humiliated, and sooner or later comes the day when they set the score to rights." He glanced to his left, spotting the bowed weary figure of Brother Vasco approaching. "But don't take my word unsupported. In a moment we may hear solid facts instead of mere deductions."

Leaning forward, he called to the Inquisitor. "Is he alive?"

"The man who tried to stop you going after Two Dogs?" Falling into a chair, Brother Vasco nodded. "Yes, he's not too badly injured to talk. And what I've learned is . . . Well, Don Miguel, I must admit it frightens me!"

"Explain!"

"They told me before I saw him that his name was Red Cloud. But when I gave him some of my relaxing draught and, as is customary, asked him how he was named to find out whether his tongue was yet unlocked by the drug, he said he was called Bloody Axe."

"And is he talking now—freely?"

"Yes, that's what I came to report to you."

"Then let's go to him, quickly, and get at the truth behind this horror!" Don Miguel jumped to his feet and strode towards the tent where the injured Mohawk was being interrogated. Angered at having to leave his chair just after sitting down, Brother Vasco followed.

The modern techniques in use by the Holy Office were, as Don Miguel had discovered while investigating the matter of the contraband Aztec mask, extremely refined, extremely subtle and almost unbelievably efficient. Knowing this, however, scarcely lessened the eerie impact of watching and hearing a man who consciously would have preferred to die rather than give away his secrets yielding full and detailed answers to every one of Brother Vasco's questions.

Two Dogs? That was an alias, the injured man said without being able to stop himself; his tribal name was Hundred Scalps, but he had most commonly been known as Broken Tree. At that one of Don Rodrigo's New World-born—but non-Mohawk—Licentiates drew breath sharply and identified the name as that of a brilliant student at the Mexicological Institute several years before.

That fitted . . .

The information obtained from Bloody Axe pieced together with the clues dropped by Father Ramón before he was killed to make a terrifying unity in Don Miguel's mind. As usual in human affairs, the crisis turned out to be rooted in the festering compost of greed.

The Confederacy of the East was only "of the East" in the sense that that was the direction in which it lay relative to the Empire. In fact, its expansion was barred on that side, partly by the contrary expansion of Cathay with its old, stable and highly evolved civilisation, partly by the hostile winters which yearly locked up so much of the territory it nominally controlled. It was small consolation to suspect that mineral wealth beyond the dreams of avarice might be discovered in Siberia, when it was buried under earth frozen to the hardness of rock. By contrast, the Empire's alliance with the Mohawk Nation gave them free access to a continent over most of which the climate was equable and whose resources had been charted at leisure during the past century and a half.

But—as Two Dogs had correctly pointed out to Don Miguel—just as there were still a handful of revanchists in England who railed against the Spanish domination of their island, so too there were Indians who resented being crammed into a single tribal category. To be a genuine Mohawk, like Red Bear, was to be the heir of a great and proud tradition; to be a courtesy Mohawk was to be deprived of both traditions and national identity.

Over the past decade or so a group of fanatical Indians out here in the very far west of North America had sought means to drive a wedge between the uneasy allies. A first and obvious step was to approach the Confederacy and let it be understood that they and their supporters would switch their allegiance in return for help. But the Confederacy was reluctant, seeing little profit for themselves in having friends on the Pacific coast of America when they had no seaboard of their own on that ocean; the Cathayans had exercised sound strategic judgement and barred all the available routes.

What persuaded them in the end was the offer of secret survey data, prepared on behalf of the Empire by Indian mineralogists like Two Dogs, showing rich veins of gold, silver and copper ore as yet unexploited by the Imperial miners. A single season's work in the past could yield hundreds of tons of valuable metal. The gamble was worth taking, especially since the Indians promised to conceal all traces of their interference. Even if by mischance some of them eventually came to light, they argued, the only consequence would be to show the world the truth about the flimsiness of the Empire-Mohawk alliance, which would splinter, and at least some of those splinters could be picked up by the Confederacy.

In return, the Indians were to be supplied with arms and money enabling them to declare a new independent state of Shasklapima, with its frontier on the Sierra Maestra, extending from Nootka Sound in the north to the southernmost tip of the California peninsula.

At least, that was the ostensible goal of the operation. In fact, as was known only to a small inner group of conspirators, there was no intention of concealing the Confederacy's theft of ore from the past. The real plan called for the deed to be pinned squarely on the perpetrators as soon as possible, and Don Miguel's arrival in New Madrid on his way to spend a furlough in California suggested an ideal opportunity.

But for the fact that Father Ramón's agents had traced the purchase of the broken drill-bit and reported it as having been bought by a Mohawk—a Mohawk subject, rather—the outcome would have been precisely what the Indians expected, especially in view of the panicky shooting of Roan Horse. A formal charge of temporal contrabandage would have been brought, and tried in a Vatican court. The only possible verdict must be one of guilty, and the Confederacy would be ordered to give an undertaking that they would never again attempt a similiar operation.

Whereupon the Indians would produce evidence upon evidence that they had broken their pledge. All over the continent there were mining sites cunningly faked by Indian time-travellers, salted with such incontrovertible proof of Confederate responsibility as knives of Augsburg steel, ale-bottles overlooked in a heap of ore-tailings, the odd coin that fell from a worker's pocket . . .

In the face of the Confederacy's frantic denials of guilt, more and more evidence of wholesale plundering would be found. Suspicion would mount, accusations would fly, perhaps even the Vatican might be deceived and support the Empire in their dispute. The injured innocence of the Confederacy would no doubt eventually turn to cynicism, determination to be hanged for a sheep rather than a nonexistent lamb.

So the likeliest outcome would be war. The millstones across the sea were to be set grinding again, and from between them—so it was assumed in the grandiose vision to which Two Dogs had dedicated himself—the unwilling subjects of the Mohawk Nation would escape into the freedom they craved. Not for them a piddling little new republic, forced to bend the knee despite its nominal independence before the world's two most powerful nations—they wanted to see the Empire and the Confederacy destroy each other, and leave Indians the masters of their own continent.

Stunned by the ingenuity of the plan and the narrowness of their escape, Don Miguel put one last question to Bloody Axe. Suppose the plan was discovered and thwarted, as indeed it had been?

The answer struck cold and hurtful as that chopping blade for which he had been named. "We took our solemn oath upon the war-drum. In that event—rather than endure the Empire's vengeance—we have sworn to bring it down around your ears, and all of history with it if need be!"

EIGHT

"We have to deal with a madman!" cried the Prince.

Don Miguel swallowed hard and gave a nod. "There's little doubt of that, sir. Two Dogs is a megalomaniac, whose ambitions have wiped out all traces of empathy from his mind."

"But why didn't the Holy Office detect this when he was a student at the Mexicological Institute? Surely insanity on that scale must have shown up like a beacon-fire on a hill-top! Brother Vasco, what have you got to say about that?"

Beside Don Miguel the Dominican shifted uneasily in his chair. In a defensive tone he said, "It appears that the full onset of his condition must be recent. Our investigations have shown that he covered his tracks very cleverly, and used many aliases which he picked according to the old Indian custom whereby a child is named for the first ominous thing the father sees after leaving the birth-teepee. He has been

variously known as Broken Tree, Hundred Scalps, Storm of
Rain, Puma Claw, and—oh, the list is longer than I can recall.
As for Bloody Axe, who passed as Red Cloud when he became
a Licentiate of the Society, his career is nearly as chequered.
Worse yet, almost sixty of the Licentiates granted their
time-licences in New Castile have proved to be associated with
one or other of these two."

"Then we have to deal not only with one madman, but with
a conspiracy of lunatics!" snapped Red Bear. His long
coppery face was shiny with sweat, and his braided hair hung
lank and dull as though tarnished with strain and worry. No
one could question his allegiance to the Empire and the
Mohawk Nation—he was pure Mohawk for ten generations
back—but it was clear he took this crisis as a personal affront.
"Moreover it seems there are lunatics outside the conspiracy
too: I mean in the Confederacy! That was what impelled me
to take a decision independently of the Full Council of the
Society, and authorise the creation of local causative loops in
order to bring us together via time apparatus rather than
waiting for the slow Atlantic passage of a ship."

Don Miguel started. Though he had been astonished to
find the General Officers here in New Madrid, he had not
realised that was how they had made the journey; he had
assumed that the Prince had sent for them some time in the
past, perhaps a month ago, and they had just reached the city.
Borromeo had sternly forbidden the use of time apparatus for
present-time journeys, and until now the rule had been
obeyed because the effect of travellers arriving fractions of a
second before they left could not be calculated.

But this crisis, granted, was without precedent ..

"I think it right that you should be told," Red Bear
continued, "that we passed news of this calamity via dip-

lomatic contacts to the Confederacy as soon as possible, and some—some *fools* over there are hindering the co-operation of the Temporal College with us, arguing that for the Empire to crash about our ears would be no bad thing for the Confederacy."

"They're out of their minds!" moaned the Prince. His face was grey with pure unmitigated terror; it was the first time Don Miguel had seen a man's face literally lose all colour. One day, he suspected, he might look in the glass on rising from one of his sleepless nights and see that same greyness on his own tanned skin.

And expressions of equal dismay were to be found on every side. This assembly was no mere private meeting in the Prince's chamber of audience; this was the first meeting of the Full Council of the Society to be held in New Madrid since the one called to establish the New Castile Chapter, sixty years ago. And, as Red Bear had just announced to those who were not party to the secret, many of them had arrived here before they left Londres. It was *that* much of an emergency. There had never been one like it. There might never be another similar—never, until the Last Judgement.

These were the sober, just and upright men appointed under the bull *De tenebris temporalibus* . . . and they were quaking in their shoes. In Don Miguel's imagination the spheres of the universe ground against each other like clock-work after a bucket of sand had been tipped in.

Mastering himself, the Prince put his trembling hands out of sight under the table and spoke again.

"Father Terence!" he exclaimed. "We must turn to you as we formerly turned to your late predecessor Father Ramón —may he rest in peace. What say you about this crisis?"

The man next to Red Bear gave a shrug. He was most of the

things that Father Ramón had not been—tall, heavily built, with a thatch of fair hair—and he spoke with a strong Irish accent. This was someone whose name had long been familiar to Don Miguel but whom he had not previously met: Father Terence O'Dubhlainn, newly senior among the Society's theoreticians.

"Doubtless Father Ramón had laid plans before his murder," he replied. "And it's probable they were apt to the situation. Deprived of his unparalleled insight, we must make what shift we can. What is absolutely certain is this: any attempt to eliminate the Indian, Two Dogs, by intervention from present time—by assassination, for example—will create a closed loop with incalculable consequences and we can regard it only as a last resort. There is no precedent for arrest and execution in past time, and it's a violation of the most cherished canons of the Society. We must accordingly elect a less dangerous alternative."

"But there's no precedent for anything until it's done the first time!" snapped Don Miguel. For a long moment he feared he had gone too far in voicing the cynical platitude; Father Terence flushed and bridled, where Father Ramón would have inclined his head and spoken with gentle reproof.

"You presume too much!" he barked. "I said we must choose a less dangerous alternative! Before shouting me down, why not hear whether we have yet discovered one?"

Memory of that New Year's Eve when Father Ramón had knowingly condemned himself to an intellectual torture whose refinement passed imagining—being responsible for actions he had not committed—drove hot words to Don Miguel's tongue-tip. But he bit them back. He was, after all, twenty years the junior of Father Terence and most of his companions.

After a final glare at his interrupter, Father Terence resumed. "One must grant that it's a first-order probability Two Dogs will decide to carry out his boast about bringing down the Empire. Accordingly, having analysed the studies he pursued under the name of Broken Tree at the Mexicological Institute and the University of New Castile, and having taken into account what Navarro tells us about his recent conversations on related subjects, we've compiled a list of probable points at which he might conclude the Empire's history was especially vulnerable. We do not exclude the risk of interference in Europe rather than the New World."

"Have you nothing more concrete to go on than these vague deductions?" the Prince demanded.

"We are lucky to have stumbled on the existence of this secret inner group of oath-bound fanatics. According to Bloody Axe there were never more than eight or ten of them all told; the remainder of the conspirators had been fobbed off with this yarn about the foundation of an independent republic and appear to have believed it sincerely." Father Terence coughed behind his hand.

"Now it's notorious that only one crucial event stood between us and oblivion in the sixteenth century. Had we not conquered England, had the Armada not made the seas safe for our invasion forces from the Netherlands, it can be logically argued that there would never have been an Empire. The renewed Moorish attacks in Spain would have reduced us to a mere satrapy of the Mediterranean Caliphate."

There were scowls of impatience around the table. Every Probationer knew what Father Terence was rehearsing at such length; the key period of the conquest of England was invariably the subject of hours of discussion and several examination questions in a first-year course of instruction, and it had been exhaustively studied by time-travellers for nearly a century.

Aware of his listeners' eagerness, Father Terence cut his discourse short. He said bluntly, "Accordingly, we recommend that all the Licentiates we can muster be set to stand guard over the events leading up to the conquest. If we fail to detect interference by Two Dogs there, we must sift through the lesser alternatives until we discover him. And only if we determine that some alteration has actually been caused in our known history should we attempt more direct action and have him arrested or assassinated."

"But if he's already interfered with history—" the Prince began.

"How will we have time to counteract the deed?" Father Terence completed the sentence for him. "It's a matter of the skewed relationship between time past and time present, sir. There's a diagonal component of durative time which will ensure a margin of error factorially dependent on the time between Two Dogs's arrival in the past and the commission of the fatal act. It will probably amount to only a few hours, but that should suffice."

"And we jump in and sabotage his trick?"

"Ideally, yes, because this will result in the past remaining unaffected."

"Hmm!" The Prince looked and sounded dubious, but he knew very well he owed his status as Commander of the Society to his royal birth rather than to any special brilliance in the field of temporal science. He turned to Red Bear and broached a different subject.

"What steps have you taken to prevent Two Dogs reaching the past?"

"Loyal men are guarding all our time apparatus, but . . ."

Red Bear scowled. "The machines are so simple to build! And even if his cronies haven't the materials to assemble their own, I wouldn't put it past those idiots in the Confederacy to help him travel back. We must assume he's already left; there are only a few grains of sand left in our hourglass, and then the scythe will descend."

There was a dull silence. The Prince broke it with a bang of his fist on the table.

"Enough talk!" he burst out. "Go find this man, in the name of God, before he wipes us all out of the universe!"

And it could happen . . . All of them knew that in theory; the General Officers and most senior Licentiates such as Don Arturo and Don Rodrigo knew it thanks to the expeditions to parallel branches of time which the Society had conducted over the past forty years—but only Don Miguel knew it in the marrow of his bones, from actual personal experience in this contemporary world. Now that Father Ramón was dead, no one else shared his recollection of that New Year's night of horror and bloodshed which, in a single bold stroke, the Jesuit had abolished from reality.

That was the kind of action this crisis called for, he was convinced: prompt, direct, incisive! Not this pussyfooting caution, like friends consulting about a game of correspondence chess! He had talked to Two Dogs for long hours, far away in California; he had formulated an opinion of him as a man, as a personality, and he *knew* this was a man who would not utter empty threats, but someone whose pride would compel him to the ultimate blasphemy of believing that he was uniquely right.

But he had no hope, he realised sickly, of persuading the General Officers to his own way of thinking. The best he

could look forward to was the survival of his world by what
would amount to a miracle, and resumption of his normal life
as a Licentiate with a trifle more experience, and a great deal
more notoriety, than the average run of his colleagues.

It was a slender bulwark to erect in his mind against the
doom-laden grinding of the heavenly spheres that night by
night made his skull ring so loudly he could not rest—only
dream terrible and dreadful dreams.

A mere couple of days elapsed—though it felt like eternity—before orders were issued for himself and his friend
Don Felipe. Like the majority of the younger Licentiates, their
brief was to patrol, in disguise and with feigned identities, the
path of events immediately preceding the departure of the
Armada from Cadiz. It made excellent sense to protect that of
all historical nexi from interference—yet somehow he could
not believe that Two Dogs would be so blatant in his attack. . .

Which was why, the evening before his departure, he met
with Don Felipe in the drinking-shop currently most popular
among the younger members of the Society in New Madrid,
and mentioned that he had written a letter.

"To Kristina?" Don Felipe said, his dark eyes darting back
and forth between the folded paper and Don Miguel's face.
"Yes, I've written also." Feeling in the pouch at his belt, he
produced a letter that might have been the twin of Don
Miguel's except that the superscription was to the Lady
Ingeborg. "But do you think there's any point in mailing
them?"

Don Miguel thought of the high-masted handsome trans-
Atlantic liners that daily bowed out of the port here into the
harsh hands of the ocean gale, and gave a shrug.

"I don't know. But I felt relieved that I had set my thoughts
on paper, even though they may never now be read. How do

you imagine it will happen, if it does? Will there be a period of fading, or instant obliteration?"

Don Felipe's face darkened. "I hope," he said soberly, "we shan't know anything . . . But there is one minor advantage, I suppose."

"What?"

"Well, according to my confessor, a soul in a potential world is classed as limbo-fodder. Which means that if Two Dogs succeeds, we shan't need to worry about paying for our little lapses from grace. Indeed we'll be kicking ourselves for not having had a bit more fun."

"Do you find that amusing?" Don Miguel said.

"No. No, honestly I don't. But I think after a few drinks I might—and what better medicine is there than laughter?"

So they called for wine and brandy, and spent their final evening together inventing ridiculous toasts to the end of the world.

NINE

Within the range over which time apparatus afforded fair accuracy—about two and a half thousand years—there were three zones of history which had exercised an obsessive fascination on temporal explorers ever since the Society was founded. One, inevitably, was the beginning of the Christian era . . . but access to Palestine of that day was severely restricted for fear that even the presence of non-intervening observers should draw the attention of the Roman authorities to the remarkable interest being generated by an unknown holy man, and cause Pilate to act earlier than the Sanhedrin, according to the written record, had desired.

The next was the downfall of Rome before the barbarian invasions; the Empire was the greatest single power to appear on Earth since the Roman heyday, and there was always the haunting suspicion that it too might be laid low. If there were clues and hints to aid survival that might be discovered by the study of their predecessors' fate, the Imperial government wanted to hear them.

And, third, there was the year of 1588 when Britain had been conquered and the existence of the Empire had thereby been rendered possible. This nexus of events was by far the most thoroughly documented period of explorable time. For that reason, when Don Miguel arrived between the crystal pillars along with the iron and silver frame which had transported him four hundred and one years into the past, he could say to himself, "Now the Armada is assembling! Despite the valiant efforts of the English who have raided its ports and tried to burn its galleons, work proceeds apace. The Duke of Parma will have a force of more than a hundred ships; he'll muster six thousand sailors and twenty thousand soldiers, and waiting in the Netherlands are as many more to launch the invasion of England."

Put in such concrete terms, the danger he had been sent here to counteract suddenly became unreal. He looked around the gracious, airy, Moorish-style courtyard of the house in which the Society had established a temporary base for the duration of the operation—purely to conceal the arrival of so many strangers, they needed a convincing cover, and could not rely on the isolation far from any town or village which ordinarily served them well enough—and felt a sense of what might be called solidity in the world. How, after all, could one man wipe out the whole of history for four mortal centuries? Two Dogs could scarcely command the weather so that the storm brewing at invasion time favoured the English rather than the Spanish fleet! He'd said so himself to some questioner or other, not many months ago—when? A brief frown crossed his face; then he remembered that it had been during the Marquesa di Jorque's party.

And he was suddenly afraid all over again. The Society had almost panicked over the matter of the contraband mask; a contraband man, so to speak, could cause infinite harm . . . say by sowing pestilence among the soldiers, by poisoning their water-barrels, by sinking a ship to block the harbour and allowing the English a chance to attack once more.

Yes, indeed, there were terrible risks to face. But it was imperative not to despair. Leaving the vicinity of the time apparatus, he spoke to the advance guard of Licentiates who had been here for three days already, local time, preparing equipment and collecting news, and was given reassuring answers to his questions.

"Yes, the work's proceeding normally. No, there's no sickness been reported. Here are your contemporary clothes and contemporary sword, and here's a briefing sheet with your instructions and a map."

The wrought-iron grilles protecting the villa the Society had rented clanged shut behind him, and he set off down the road in the direction of the harbour. Cadiz was a fair-sized city, even this far back, and it was a considerable walk to his destination, especially since the streets were thronged with foot-passengers, pack-animals and wagons too large for the width of the carriageway, but the more he saw of his surroundings the better he felt. There was absolutely no difference between this bustling city and what the historical record showed; this was the place that had launched the Armada . . . in spite of the threats of Two Dogs. Besides, this was a more reassuring area of the past to visit than the others he'd been sent to: Imperial Rome, Macedonia under Alexander, Texcoco to replace the stolen mask. He was speaking a form of Spanish, though he had to be careful to amend his accent if he spoke to one of the natives and avoid anachronistic words; he was walking ground some of his ancestors had doubtless also trodden, and for the first time, moreover. He began to imagine that he might once again remember how to be cheerful.

His brief had been short and pointed: he was to go to the harbour and tour it from end to end, hunting for the least discrepancy that might betray interference. Despite the noontide heat he did so, unchallenged because he was garbed as an obviously wealthy minor noble and wore a sword meant for use rather than show, with a dent or two in the guard at its hilt. Protected from over-close scrutiny by his deliberately arrogant manner, he maintained a slightly bored expression as he walked, but in fact he was marvelling at the spectacle. Those galleons with their high proud masts, those gun-ports ready to snort death, those tidily drilled soldiers carrying their kit aboard by platoons, all those hogsheads of pickled meat and barrels of water and biscuit, all those great wagonloads of powder and shot—real! Solid! Unchanged from what they should have been!

Three hours passed, and at last he dared to let himself hope. Here, at least, the effect of anything Two Dogs might have tried was not apparent. Possibly he had failed in his endeavours; it was risky for untrained travellers to wander about the past—perilous enough, indeed, for the Society's hand-picked Licentiates. But that was being over-optimistic. More likely, he'd realised that the Society would hasten to patrol this weakest spot in the Empire's history and chosen a second-best point of attack. But there was nowhere that offered a satisfactory alternative. With this particular episode protected, the Empire was like a man wearing good sound body-armour; immune to stabs in the heart or belly or lungs, he need fear only injury, not certain death.

His spirits lightening as he reached this conclusion, and extremely thirsty after his three-hour tour of the harbour, Don Miguel turned into a humble wine-shop whose proprietor almost fainted to see such a finely-dressed customer and fawned over him nauseatingly, uttering many oaths concerning the quality of his wine and the cleanliness of his premises. In fact the wine was nasty and the whole place was smeared with grime, but Don Miguel was in no mood to worry over trifles.

"Of course, your honour, we've been so busy lately," the landlord muttered as he strove vainly to mop enough dirt off a chair-seat to save it marking Don Miguel's breeches. "All day and all night they've been coming in, the soldiers and sailors, and not a few of their officers as well . . . Wine, your honour! Here it comes—let me pour it for you . . ." He did so with an inept flourish. "Would you care for *tapas*? We have good crayfish today, and mussels too!"

Thinking of the raw sewage that poured into the sea where the shellfish grew, Don Miguel refused, but gulped the wine gratefully; lemon-juice would have helped his thirst, and this was not *quite* so sour.

"Is your honour one of the officers sailing with the fleet, then?" the landlord probed. Silence had overtaken his three other customers—all of them petty merchants, by their appearance, probably suppliers contracting for provisions to stock the ships—and he seemed a little nervous.

"No, but I came to look over the preparations and to drink to their good fortune." Don Miguel raised his mug cheerfully in the direction of his fellow-customers. "How say you to that, my friends?"

"Why, your honour, no loyal Spaniard or good Catholic

would do otherwise than echo you!" answered the nearest of them, a beetle-browed fellow with one shoulder higher than the other. "But let me ask your honour this, first! Though of course the true faith is bound to triumph, are you honestly sanguine of this venture?"

A tremor of apprehension prickled on Don Miguel's nape. He said, "Indeed I am! Why in the world should we not foresee a great victory for the Armada?"

"With a commander who's sick at the least lurching of his ship?" The beetle-browed man swigged his wine and wiped his mouth with the back of his hand. "I'm of a seafaring family myself, your honour, though now I've been forced to work ashore thanks to this bad back of mine." He jerked his high shoulder back and forth. "And I've been told all my life, by my father and his father before him: a ship's crew is only as good as the captain. And isn't the same thing true of a fleet?"

Don Miguel said faintly, "His Grace the Duke of Parma—"

"Parma? What are you talking about?" Instantly the entire company was alert: the beetle-browed man, his two companions, the landlord and even the small boy armed with a jug and a greasy rag who stood hidden in the shadows by the racked wine-barrels at the rear of the shop. "Parma's in the Netherlands, your honour! Medina Sidonia's in charge of this fleet, and a worse sea-commander could hardly be picked in the whole of Spain!"

With those words, Don Miguel Navarro became the first man to realise that the universe was crumbling about him, except always for Two Dogs, and Two Dogs had desired it should be so.

The Duke of Parma in the Netherlands? This wasn't history! The Duke of Parma, Spain's finest military commander of the century, took the Armada to sea! Medina Sidonia—who was he? A nonentity, an entry in the footnotes of the history books! And the Netherlands were secured permanently for Spain and its heir the Empire by that brilliant unorthodox master of strategy, the Scottish Catholic Earl of Barton, who when the Armada broke the English resistance at sea was prepared with his hundreds of flat-bottomed barges to land an army of fifteen thousand men in Kent and shatter the resistance on land as well.

Why in the name of all that was holy had they been persuaded to waste Parma on a footling land-war?

He said after such a pause he fancied he had heard the grinding of Earth on its axis, "And the Earl of Barton—does he serve with Parma in the Netherlands?"

By now the others in the wine-shop were exchanging puzzled glances, at a loss to know how a finely-dressed gentleman could be so out of touch with the news. Uncertainly the landlord said, "Perhaps, perhaps! It's not a name I know."

"To me it sounds like an English name!" The beetle-browed man rose to his feet. Moving away from his table, he went on, "Who are you, that you ask such peculiar questions?" He had abandoned the formal "your honour."

"Ah . . ." Trying to appear calm, Don Miguel drained his wine-mug and also rose. "I've been travelling. A long time. I just reached Cadiz and welcomed the chance to see the fleet before it sailed. But now I have pressing business. My score, landlord!"

"Not so quickly," the beetle-browed man snapped. "Landlord, we should fetch a patrol, in my view. For all we know this fellow may be an English spy."

"Nonsense!" Don Miguel tossed a gold coin towards the landlord. "But—"

"You speak strangely. Doesn't he speak strangely?" The beetle-browed man appealed to the others. "I think we ought to hold him until he's been interrogated!"

Don Miguel's patience broke, and he darted for the door. The beetle-browed man tried to stop him, hobbling to block the way, but as well as being deformed he limped, and he was too slow—Don Miguel went past him and out into the street at a headlong run.

Although reason told him running could do little to speed his purpose.

TEN

Mind pounding faster than his feet, he outstripped even the shouts the suspicious men in the wine-shop hurled after him on the way back to the villa the Society had picked for its local base. This was what he had wanted to say to the General Officers, and been unable to cast into words that would gain their attention: that Two Dogs was devious and brilliant, that he *would* strike where the Empire was most vulnerable—but he would not do it in the way the Society most expected. Not for him the crudity of the bludgeon. He preferred the delicacy of a scalpel.

And he'd found one. Before God he'd found one so sharp its wound would kill before the feather-touch of the blade was felt!

He'd taken out of history a man about whom almost nothing was known.

Or to be exact, about whom little was known except

legend . . .

As they learned the tales of El Cid or Roland and Oliver, all schoolboys in the Empire could recount how the Earl of Barton had made his first appearance on the world scene: a youth of twenty owning his clothes, a horse and a sword, claiming to be related on the wrong side of the blanket to the House of Stewart—like countless others—and determined to revenge the extermination of his Catholic relatives in Scotland by troops of the Protestant Queen Elizabeth. Given his opportunity thanks to the death of his general during a battle in which he rallied the Catholic forces from almost certain defeat, he proved himself the finest strategist of his age, and his troops developed an almost superstitious loyalty to him. When Parma was recalled to command the Armada, he was the obvious choice as deputy, and made sure for ever of the Netherlands in sixteen weeks of whirlwind campaigning which laid the enemy low like wheat before the reaper's scythe.

Take him away, and . . . who was left instead?

That *must* be the point at which Two Dogs had struck—not here, by any means as crude as poisoning the water-barrels.

Surely, though, someone who had exerted such an influence on the establishment of the Empire must have been the subject of exhaustive study by the Society? Probably his movements from birth to death had been secretly documented. All it would take would be half an hour's research, and the Licentiates deployed here at Cadiz and over in England could be dispatched instead to guard—

—*a man who already had never existed.*

For a second that realisation stopped him in his tracks, like a physical blow. He grew briefly aware that the townsfolk were staring at him, wondering what made a finely-dressed gentleman race through their streets as though pursued by devils, and ignored them. Breaking anew into a run, he struggled to discipline his mind back into the laboriously learned techniques of five-dimensional thinking he had been drilled through as a Probationer in the Society.

Two Dogs had almost certainly killed the Earl of Barton; he would have wanted to make his work definitive. Perhaps he'd located the Earl as a child, or on his way to join the Spanish forces in the Netherlands. It didn't matter. At this juncture, June of 1588, the consequences of the action were already being experienced. They must be welling down the ages ahead of him like an incoming tide, along the curious skew-axis of hypothetical or speculative time—the medium in which existed improbable alternative worlds Father Ramón had told him of. There was a sort of inertia implicit in the process; the alteration of history was a sluggish event because it was *not* an event—it did not occur in ordinary time.

Up ahead in the twentieth century, there might even yet be time apparatus under the control of Red Bear and Father Terence, waiting to fetch back Licentiates from Cadiz in the sixteenth century. If so, if only the echo of the murder of Lord Barton had not "by now" durated to destroy the Society altogether, he still stood a slim chance of warning them in time and having Two Dogs killed before he could leave for the past—if necessary having him shot off the back of the horse he'd ridden away from his mine in California. That too would alter history, but at least it would be altered back towards the unmodified version.

Whereupon there would once again be an Earl of Barton and everything would revert to normal.

Perhaps!

He stormed up the final slope to the Society's rented villa

and screamed at the gate-keeper to hurry and let him in. Not waiting for the formalities, he thrust past the man and shouted at the top of his lungs to everyone in earshot, "There isn't an Earl of Barton in this world!"

The impact was immediate. Busy with a score of different tasks, Licentiates and worried young Probationers dashed to the courtyard in the centre of the house where the time apparatus stood, and heard the story in fragments from Don Miguel as the technicians rapidly reversed their equipment and arranged his return to the future. There was no point in sending a message; a man would get there just as quickly and would be more informative.

Don Miguel was almost crying with impatience when at last the settings were correct and his surroundings suddenly looked as though they were melting, indicating that he was being twisted in the continuum, that time was becoming a direction along which the forces constrained within the frame of iron and silver drove him like a metal rod between the closing blades of a pair of scissors. The distorted outline of the cage of bars itself became more visible, more *convincing*, as he was hurtled forward.

No time apparatus could go further towards the future than the moment at which it was energised, nor could an object or a person contained within it. The mere fact that he had left Cadiz meant that, up ahead, at "this" moment there still must be a Society of Time, for this was the same apparatus as one in the Society's office at New Madrid; he merely occupied it at a different moment.

A vast relief overcame him, yet did not completely dispel his anxiety. He fretted and fumed at the length of the journey and wished there was room for him to pace up and down; it was going to take some while to arrive, because he was being displaced through space to New Castile as well as towards the future, and inside the cage space was experienced as though it were ordinary time.

Still, this gave him a chance to calm himself and order his thoughts. On re-emerging into the twentieth century, he must speak clearly, concisely and convincingly to the General Officers, because he might overtake the onrushing tide of consequences stemming from Lord Barton's murder by only a tiny margin—by perhaps a mere hour or two! It all depended on how long ago (meaning before the start of this trip from 1588) Two Dogs had killed his victim. He might even not have departed for the past at the time when Don Miguel returned to the present, in which case the paradoxes would be giddying!

His legs ached after his frantic run from the harbour. He squatted down on the floor of the cage and tried to make himself understand the psychology of someone like Two Dogs, who didn't care if the whole structure of history collapsed because he had been frustrated in his ambitions. It wasn't so much like the tales and legends of the Red Indians which he'd studied both as a child in school and more recently as an adult while being briefed for the trip to Texcoco during which he'd restored the stolen mask. It was more like the Teutonic and Norse legends of the *Ragna Rökkr*, the twilight of the gods, where all the nine worlds crashed into chaos and spawned a new creation.

But that line of thought led him to wistful memories of Kristina, and it would be a long while before they both met again. He drove himself back to contemplation of the mind of Two Dogs, and concluded that even if the Society was compelled to put an end to his life, it would not be murder, nor even assassination. It would be execution. It would be justified because he, Don Miguel, had really been into the world where his crime had been committed, and could swear on the cross that he had seen . . . what he had seen.

And, on the subject of seeing: what was wrong with the bars surrounding him? They were always misty and deformed in transit, but they should have been growing clearer and better defined as he drew closer to the present. Instead, they seemed to be more blurred than before.

He told himself it was a trick of the eyes, and went back to planning his report to the General Officers. He dared not touch the semi-solid bars to confirm what vision indicated; that was a quick way to die, for vast energies were trapped in their configuration.

No, it was all going to come out right. Two Dogs would be stopped at some convenient point before he could set out in search of Lord Barton, and the world would return to normal, and there would be a fresh approach to the Temporal College, and this idea of breaking up the alliance with the Mohawks—

"Oh my *God*!" he cried aloud.

There had been a wrenching. It had acted on his bare brain, so that he perceived it as pain, and as blinding light, and as a sound which made his skull reverberate; as a blazing fire, as a dive for Arctic water, as a headlong fall into illimitable abysses one beyond the other without number or end.

That was the most terrible thing of all: that it was endless, and yet, after an eternity, it was over.

He had sight, and hearing, and touch, and the awareness of his body. He looked, listened, felt air and warm sunlight, knew he was physically whole, knew he had weight and substance. And while his mind still echoed with the scream of a dying universe he wanted more than anything to fall down and weep like a little child.

But that, said a small voice far distant at the edge of his awareness, is a foolish thing to do. It can be understood what has happened. Think! Think that in less than one short century after Borromeo, the world you thought of as ultimately real spawned not only Two Dogs, but others beside who played with time-travel like a nursery toy. Think of the New Year's Eve when a king was killed because of a silly quarrel. Think of the avarice that led to the theft of the Aztec mask, and what had to be done to set that right. Think why, in the world you imagined to be real, no one had come back from the future to investigate that future's past . . .

True! Merciful God, as true as daylight, and never understood—except perhaps by bitter, downcast Borromeo, who once said he was disappointed that no one from tomorrow had come to compliment him on his discovery. If a span of under a century had brought about so many abortive interferences with the past, why had not the future, with its incalculable toll of years during which time-travel would be possible?

Because there *was* no future. Not rooted in his world. Don Miguel Navarro drew breath deep into his throat and whispered the words, to make himself accept the facts.

He could visualise the path of history in each of those innumerable potential worlds where man had gained the power to travel through time. (Perhaps they were all potential, none more "real" than any other?) It would lead always back upon itself, like a snake swallowing its own tail. Man being what he was, there would sooner or later come a moment when the temptation to amend the past would lure someone into tampering with the course of events which led to the actual discovery of time apparatus. Whereupon a new universe would form.

But in that case, what had happened to him? He could almost grasp the explanation but not quite. He must, he reasoned, have been trapped between "actual" and "potential" during his journey; it must have been "after" he left Cadiz in 1588, and "before" he reached New Madrid in 1989, that the effects of Two Dogs's interference became perceptible at the latter date. In other words, he had crossed the ripple on the stream of time . . . and here he was on the other side.

What then had become of all the people he had known? Felipe, who had sat drinking with him last night, as it seemed; Kristina, who had made him the unwitting instrument of just such a loop in time as he was considering now—and who might have been a lifetime companion; the King, the Princes, the General Officers, the Margrave von Feuerstein, even Two Dogs himself? Why should they have been abolished from the total scheme of things, while he by a freak was left in possession of his knowledge and his life?

Only such a man as Father Ramón might attempt the question—and even in the universe which Two Dogs had brought crashing down, Father Ramón was dead.

Passive, he began to study his surroundings. He was in a sort of park, apparently. People were coming towards him, no doubt attracted by what to them was his extraordinary appearance, for they were dressed in outlandish garb resembling none he had ever encountered. He saw young women among them as well as men, hatless and with their legs bare above the knee, clinging shamelessly to the bare arms of their companions. Behind them he saw a city: towers of a tallness he had never dreamed of. And there were sounds he could not identify, which seemed to have their source in the sky.

He looked up. Something was passing, stiff-winged, far vaster than a bird. A mystery!

Now the people were gathering around him, a matter of a pace or two away. A man of about his own age addressed him, presumably putting a question, but the words meant nothing to Don Miguel. He countered with a question of his own.

"*Donde estoy?*" Not that he needed to be told his geographical location; this must be what corresponded to New Madrid in his own year 1988 or 1989, for if he had fallen short in time he would have fallen short in space as well and more than likely drowned in the ocean. But what did they call their city?

The man frowned. "*Español!* Ah! You are in New York!" He spoke slowly and clearly, as to an idiot, and Don Miguel gave a solemn nod. Not "New Madrid" but "Nueva Jorque" —and they spoke a form of English, the debased tongue which in his world barely survived among the peasants.

Well, what else would you expect from the defeat of the Armada?

Now, having decided that he wasn't dangerous, the rest of the onlookers were relaxing and passing excited comments. Their agitation suggested that in this world time-travel might not be known—if it had been, it would supply a ready-made explanation for the arrival of a strangely-clad man out of thin air. The idea brought with it a sense of peace, a feeling of security which he could not remember having enjoyed since Father Ramón first admitted to him how dangerous Borromeo's legacy had become.

In that event, then, let them explain his presence how they would; let them regard him as a madman, a simpleton, a foreign spy! He would never—he swore so silently to himself— afford them an inkling of the truth. He could describe the principle of time apparatus; given a ton of iron and half a ton of silver, he could build one with his own hands in a week. He would not. Whatever might be the faults of this world, it was not for men to usurp the divine prerogative and alter the order established by what had gone before.

The man who had first addressed him was beckoning, inviting him to come away. Don Miguel gave a slow smile. For better or worse, without chance of change, this was his reality now.

Don Miguel Navarro, formerly Licentiate in Ordinary of the Society of Time, now the most isolated of all the outcasts the human race had ever known, walked forward, into the real world.

Also in Hamlyn Paperbacks

Richard Lewis

SPIDERS

Out of the earth crept mankind's oldest nightmare.

The Kentish countryside was bathed in golden sunshine. All around lay peace and tranquillity.

Maybe it was too peaceful, too ominously quiet, but who'd complain about that? Certainly not old Dan Mason, energetically tugging out weeds in the farmhouse garden.

What he'd uncovered there didn't alarm him. But it should have. For he'd just released a seething army of death . . .

Also in Hamlyn Paperbacks

Guy N. Smith
author of **Night of the Crabs**

LOCUSTS

It seems the start of a glorious summer as Alan Alton and his family settle into their new home in the Shropshire hills.

Then the insects start to appear.

First there's one ... then hundreds ... thousands ... millions. A smothering tide of destruction covers the land.

LOCUSTS

As the heat-wave continues mercilessly week after week, the horde of invaders grows – a hideous, red-eyed devastation spreading across town and country.

Biting, stripping, devouring ... and hating.

Before this onslaught the human population turns to flight. As panic grows, the death-toll also rises and the whole country is plunged into chaos. Britain is being eaten alive.

Can nothing stop the locusts?

Also in Hamlyn Paperbacks

Matt Chisholm

THE TUCSON CONSPIRACY

They gambled bloodily with the lives of innocent men and women . . .

They used mayhem and murder to fulfil their ambitions . . .

The prize in their deadly gamble was the Territory of Arizona. Law and order rested in the hands of Joe Blade, lovely Charity Clayton and veteran scout George McMasters. The Tucson Ring had penetrated all walks of life in the Territory. Only two men and a woman stood between them and power.

Also in Hamlyn Paperbacks

Patricia Highsmith

THOSE WHO WALK AWAY

What do you do when someone is desperately trying to kill you? When he blames you for his daughter's suicide?

Roy Garrett has no idea why his wife killed herself. He only knows that her father now detests him so much that he will stop at nothing until Garrett ends up a corpse floating in the Grand Canal.

Among the dark alleys and piazzas of Venice begins a long and bitter duel, a pernicious game of hide-and-seek between two guilty men. This is a story of hatred, misdirected love and inevitable humiliation.

'The setting is Venice, the characterisation brilliant, the style spare and superb' – **Daily Mail**

Also in Hamlyn Paperbacks

Michael Gilbert

BLOOD AND JUDGMENT

One misty November evening a woman's body is
found near a reservoir by three boys collecting
firewood for Guy Fawkes night. She turns out to
be the wife of Monk Ritchie, an escaped criminal –
and she has been murdered.

Detective-Sergeant Patrick Petrella has a personal
interest in the case, for his colleague still lies un-
conscious after a beating up by one of Ritchie's
gang. Petrella's enthusiasm leads him to working
overtime, by night diving in the reservoir.

And though he comes up with a sunken boat, and a
body – and the murder weapon – it nearly puts paid
to his promising career.

"*Blood and Judgment* must be one of Michael
Gilbert's best ... the story combines plausibility
with such wickedly clever plotting" – **Stanley Ellin**

A HAMLYN *Whodunnit*

FICTION

HORROR/OCCULT/NASTY

☐ Death Walkers	Gary Brandner	£1.00
☐ The Howling	Gary Brandner	£1.00
☐ Return of the Howling	Gary Brandner	95p
☐ Dying Light	Evan Chandler	85p
☐ The Sanctuary	Glenn Chandler	£1.00
☐ Crown of Horn	Louise Cooper	£1.25
☐ Curse	Daniel Farson	95p
☐ Trance	Joy Fielding	90p
☐ Rattlers	Joseph L. Gilmore	95p
☐ Slither	John Halkin	95p
☐ The Wicker Man	R. Hardy & A. Shaffer	£1.25
☐ Devil's Coach-Horse	Richard Lewis	85p
☐ Spiders	Richard Lewis	80p
☐ Gate of Fear	Lewis Mallory	£1.00
☐ The Book of Shadows	Marc Olden	£1.25
☐ The Summoning	John Pintoro	95p
☐ Bloodthirst	Mark Ronson	£1.00
☐ Ghoul	Mark Ronson	95p
☐ Ogre	Mark Ronson	95p
☐ Childmare	Nick Sharman	£1.00
☐ The Scourge	Nick Sharman	£1.00
☐ Deathbell	Guy N. Smith	£1.00
☐ Doomflight	Guy N. Smith	£1.10
☐ The Specialist	Jasper Smith	£1.00

SCIENCE FICTION

☐ Clash by Night	Henry Kuttner	95p
☐ Drinking Sapphire Wine	Tanith Lee	£1.25
☐ Journey	Marta Randall	£1.00

HAMLYN WHODUNNITS

☐ The Case of the Abominable Snowman	Nicholas Blake	£1.10
☐ The Worm of Death	Nicholas Blake	95p
☐ Tour de Force	Christianna Brand	£1.10
☐ A Lonely Place to Die	Wessel Ebersohn	£1.10
☐ The Judas Pair	Jonathan Gash	95p
☐ Blood and Judgment	Michael Gilbert	£1.10
☐ There Came Both Mist and Snow	Michael Innes	95p
☐ The Weight of the Evidence	Michael Innes	£1.10
☐ Inspector Ghote Draws a Line	H. R. F. Keating	£1.10
☐ The Perfect Murder	H. R. F. Keating	£1.10
☐ The Siamese Twin Mystery	Ellery Queen	95p
☐ The Spanish Cape Mystery	Ellery Queen	£1.10

GENERAL

☐ Chains	Justin Adams	£1.25
☐ Secrets	F. Lee Bailey	£1.25
☐ The Last Liberator	John Clive	£1.25
☐ Wyndward Passion	Norman Daniels	£1.35
☐ Rich Little Poor Girl	Terence Feely	£1.50
☐ Abingdon's	Michael French	£1.25
☐ The Moviola Man	Bill and Colleen Mahan	£1.25
☐ Running Scared	Gregory Mcdonald	85p
☐ Gossip	Marc Olden	£1.25
☐ The Red Raven	Lilli Palmer	£1.25
☐ The Sounds of Silence	Judith Richards	£1.00
☐ Summer Lightning	Judith Richards	£1.25
☐ The Hamptons	Charles Rigdon	£1.35
☐ The Affair of Nina B.	Simmel	95p
☐ The Berlin Connection	Simmel	£1.50
☐ The Cain Conspiracy	Simmel	£1.20
☐ Double Agent—Triple Cross	Simmel	£1.35
☐ Celestial Navigation	Anne Tyler	£1.00
☐ Searching for Caleb	Anne Tyler	£1.00

FICTION

CRIME/ADVENTURE/SUSPENSE

☐ The Cool Cottontail	John Ball	£1.00
☐ In the Heat of the Night	John Ball	£1.00
☐ Johnny Get Your Gun	John Ball	£1.00
☐ The Killing in the Market	John Ball & B. Smith	£1.00
☐ Siege	Peter Cave	£1.15
☐ The Execution	Oliver Crawford	90p
☐ All The Queen's Men	Guiy de Montfort	£1.25
☐ Barracuda	Irving A. Greenfield	£1.25
☐ Don't Be No Hero	Leonard Harris	£1.25
☐ The Blunderer	Patricia Highsmith	£1.25
☐ A Game for the Living	Patricia Highsmith	£1.25
☐ Those Who Walk Away	Patricia Highsmith	£1.25
☐ The Tremor of Forgery	Patricia Highsmith	£1.25
☐ The Two Faces of January	Patricia Highsmith	£1.25
☐ Shearwater	Michael Jahn	£1.00
☐ The Hunted	Elmore Leonard	£1.25
☐ The Golden Grin	Colin Lewis	£1.00
☐ Labyrinth	Eric Mackenzie-Lamb	£1.25
☐ The Traitor Machine	Max Marquis	£1.25
☐ Clinton is Assigned	Malcolm McConnell	£1.25
☐ Confess, Fletch	Gregory Mcdonald	90p
☐ Fletch	Gregory Mcdonald	90p
☐ Flynn	Gregory Mcdonald	95p
☐ To Kill a Jogger	Jon Messmann	95p
☐ Pandora Man	Kerry Newcomb and Frank Schaefer	£1.25
☐ Sigmet Active	Thomas Page	£1.10
☐ The Jericho Commandment	James Patterson	£1.00
☐ Games	Bill Pronzini	£1.00
☐ Crash Landing	Mark Regan	95p
☐ The Mole	Dan Sherman	£1.25
☐ Swann	Dan Sherman	£1.00
☐ The Peking Pay-Off	Ian Stewart	90p
☐ The Seizing of Singapore	Ian Stewart	£1.00
☐ Winter Stalk	James L. Stowe	£1.25
☐ The Wolves Came Down From The Mountain	Michael Strong	£1.00
☐ Rough Deal	Walter Winward	£1.10
☐ The Ten-Tola Bars	Burton Wohl	90p

HISTORICAL ROMANCE/ROMANCE/SAGA

☐ Flowers of Fire	Stephanie Blake	£1.00
☐ So Wicked My Desire	Stephanie Blake	£1.50
☐ Morgana	Marie Buchanan	£1.35
☐ The Enchanted Land	Jude Deveraux	£1.50
☐ Mystic Rose	Patricia Gallagher	£1.25
☐ Love's Scarlet Banner	Fiona Harrowe	£1.25
☐ Lily of the Sun	Sandra Heath	95p
☐ Daneclere	Pamela Hill	£1.25
☐ Strangers' Forest	Pamela Hill	£1.00
☐ Royal Mistress	Patricia Campbell Horton	£1.50
☐ The Flight of the Dove	Catherine MacArthur	95p
☐ The Far Side of Destiny	Dore Mullen	£1.50
☐ Summer Blood	Anne Rudeen	£1.25

HAMLYN WHODUNNITS

☐ The Case of the Abominable Snowman	Nicholas Blake	£1.10
☐ The Worm of Death	Nicholas Blake	95p
☐ Tour de Force	Christianna Brand	£1.10
☐ A Lonely Place to Die	Wessel Ebersohn	£1.10
☐ The Judas Pair	Jonathan Gash	95p
☐ Blood and Judgment	Michael Gilbert	£1.10
☐ There Came Both Mist and Snow	Michael Innes	95p
☐ The Weight of the Evidence	Michael Innes	£1.10
☐ Inspector Ghote Draws A Line	H. R. F. Keating	£1.10
☐ The Perfect Murder	H. R. F. Keating	£1.10
☐ The Siamese Twin Mystery	Ellery Queen	95p
☐ The Spanish Cape Mystery	Ellery Queen	£1.10

FICTION

GENERAL

☐	Chains	Justin Adams	£1.25
☐	Secrets	F. Lee Bailey	£1.25
☐	The Last Liberator	John Clive	£1.25
☐	Wyndward Passion	Norman Daniels	£1.35
☐	Rich Little Poor Girl	Terence Feely	£1.50
☐	Abingdon's	Michael French	£1.25
☐	The Moviola Man	Bill and Colleen Mahan	£1.25
☐	Running Scared	Gregory Mcdonald	85p
☐	Gossip	Marc Olden	£1.25
☐	The Red Raven	Lilli Palmer	£1.25
☐	The Sounds of Silence	Judith Richards	£1.00
☐	Summer Lightning	Judith Richards	£1.25
☐	The Hamptons	Charles Rigdon	£1.35
☐	The Affair of Nina B.	Simmel	95p
☐	The Berlin Connection	Simmel	£1.50
☐	The Cain Conspiracy	Simmel	£1.20
☐	Double Agent—Triple Cross	Simmel	£1.35
☐	Celestial Navigation	Anne Tyler	£1.00
☐	Searching for Caleb	Anne Tyler	£1.00

WESTERN BLADE SERIES

☐	No. 1 The Indian Incident	Matt Chisholm	75p
☐	No. 2 The Tucson Conspiracy	Matt Chisholm	75p
☐	No. 3 The Laredo Assignment	Matt Chisholm	75p
☐	No. 4 The Pecos Manhunt	Matt Chisholm	75p
☐	No. 5 The Colorado Virgins	Matt Chisholm	85p
☐	No. 6 The Mexican Proposition	Matt Chisholm	85p
☐	No. 7 The Arizona Climax	Matt Chisholm	85p
☐	No. 8 The Nevada Mustang	Matt Chisholm	85p
☐	No. 9 The Montana Deadlock	Matt Chisholm	85p
☐	No. 10 The Cheyenne Trap	Matt Chisholm	95p
☐	No. 11 The Navaho Trail	Matt Chisholm	95p

WAR

☐	The Andersen Assault	Peter Leslie	£1.25
☐	Killers Under a Cruel Sky	Peter Leslie	£1.25
☐	Jenny's War	Jack Stoneley	£1.25

NAVAL HISTORICAL

☐	HMS Bounty	John Maxwell	£1.00
☐	The Mary Celeste	John Maxwell	£1.00
☐	The Baltic Convoy	Showell Styles	95p

SCIENCE FICTION

☐	Clash by Night	Henry Kuttner	95p
☐	Drinking Sapphire Wine	Tanith Lee	£1.25
☐	Journey	Marta Randall	£1.00

NAME ....

ADDRESS...

....

Write to Hamlyn Paperbacks Cash Sales, PO Box 11, Falmouth, Cornwall TR10 9EN.

Please indicate order and enclose remittance to the value of the cover price plus:

U.K.: Please allow 40p for the first book, 18p for the second book and 13p for each additional book ordered, to a maximum charge of £1.49.

B.F.P.O. & EIRE: Please allow 40p for the first book, 18p for the second book plus 13p per copy for the next 7 books, thereafter 7p per book.

OVERSEAS: Please allow 60p for the first book plus 18p per copy for each additional book.

Whilst every effort is made to keep prices low it is sometimes necessary to increase cover prices and also postage and packing rates at short notice. Hamlyn Paperbacks reserve the right to show new retail prices on covers which may differ from those previously advertised in the text or elsewhere.